MW00885184

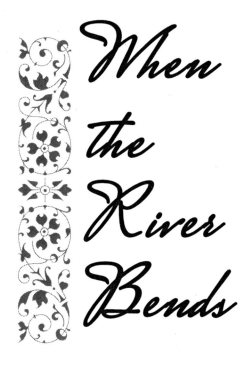

When the River Bends

Ann DeChellis

To Kalee –
Start Wrighting.

Ann DeChellis

Copyright © 2014 Ann DeChellis
All rights reserved
First Edition

PAGE PUBLISHING, INC.
New York, NY

First originally published by Page Publishing, Inc. 2014

ISBN 978-1-63417-396-4 (pbk)
ISBN 978-1-63417-397-1 (digital)

Printed in the United States of America

To my children, whom I love dearly and I am proud of.
To my mom, who truly loved me unto her death, and I her.
To God, who always has me in the palm of His hand.

CONTENTS

PROLOGUE

EVERYONE HAS THEIR OWN WAY of viewing life. I look at it as a journey down a river. It would be great if we could fly over the top of it to see all the bends and turns, the rocks and rapids before we hit them. We could prepare ourselves for the rough parts, and when the very sharp bends in the river come, we could just hold on for dear life. But what would we learn from that? Nothing! If God gave us all the answers to the tests, how could He teach us? How would we grow?

I look back now, and I can see clearly that when I was drowning, God always threw me a life preserver even when I couldn't see through the thick fog. He was always there helping me to get up and starting me on the river of life again.

CHAPTER 1

The Meeting

I WAS GRADUATING FROM HIGH school and just eighteen years old when I met Mat DeChallis. I was raised in a small town where your life didn't go much further than the city limits. I was from a family of five girls, all dark-haired, and no boys. The oldest is Jean, a free-spirited, smart, sassy, fiery type. Next is Kathy, very quick-witted, a charmer, and a home-body. Then comes Karen always shooting from the hip, loud-mouthed, on the wild side! I am no. 4, Ann. I'm a strong-willed person with a lot of humor, somewhat quick-witted with common sense and a strong love for God. I also have a compassionate heart, which usually gets me more in trouble. I have green and blue eyes mixed and stormy like the sea! Last is Beth. The mistake baby. You know, when Mom and

Dad thought they were done, and surprise! Beth has common sense but wants to control everyone and everything.

My poor dad! He always had male dogs.

My big dream was to go to college and live on campus and get a degree. But my parents did not have the means to send me, and in those days, you did not take loans. So my plan was to go into retail management with the plant nursery business and make some money to pay for my school. *Boom!* In walked Mat who also worked there. He was a good-looking man and six and a half years older than me. He had dark curly hair, a mustache, and a real lean build on his almost six-foot frame. He had big, brown, beautiful eyes. When we were introduced, Mat was rude and quite snobbish at first; but as the week went by, things warmed up. I was taking college classes, and I had just bought a used VW Bug, and it was a stick shift. I seriously did not know how to drive this car. Mat also had a stick shift, and he offered his help. I was glad to get it.

Within one week, we started dating. On our first date, I asked him to go walking on some nice grounds. He was very much a gentleman. He dropped me off at home and just said good night. The second date was to see a movie. Nothing big. Again, he dropped me off and gave me a little hug. I wanted to kiss him, but I guessed he was being polite. Third date same thing, he held my hand and a little hug. I went into the house, and my mother was waiting for me.

"How did it go, honey?"

"This guy is so slow, Mom. He still hasn't kissed me."

"Oh, he's just being a gentleman."

"Well, it's getting old."

I began to think Mat knew I was getting impatient. On our fourth date, he kissed me. Within six months of meeting each other, Mat asked me to marry him. I was nineteen years old and head over heels in love! I always found it odd that he asked me to marry him and he didn't have a ring yet. I was so in love I didn't care. Our families were told the next day, and the wedding was planned—a very big Italian wedding with almost three hundred guests. We picked out things together.

I had just turned twenty, and Mat was twenty-six and a half. I was very sick at our wedding. I had a kidney infection, and it was diagnosed wrong for a long time, but the huge Italian wedding with all the trimmings went on. We had planned it together, but mostly me and my mom.

We drove out east for our honeymoon, and right in the middle of it, I became very ill with fever. Mat drove home and took me right to the hospital where they misdiagnosed me again.

For our first year of marriage, I was very ill because my kidneys were getting worse, but I did not know it. I always felt Mat was such a great guy for not demanding sex when I was so sick. In fact, I thought he was wonderful. Finally, a little over a year into our marriage, I was hospitalized because I was so sick. They finally found the real problem. By that time, my kidneys were twice the size they were supposed to be. I was anemic, and I had pneumonia in both lungs. I was treated, and I made a full recovery. Things were going well, and two years into marriage we bought our starter home. It was a real fixer-upper. Mat and I worked really hard to make a home. No children yet, but I had now become a hairstylist to save money to go to school with. We were both working hard to start our lives.

Four years married, now it felt like we were starting to feel the bumps in marriage.

"Mat, why don't we go mess around for a while? I'm feeling a little horny."

"Not tonight, Ann."

"OK, never mind." All the time I was thinking, what man in his early thirties says that?

It was late March, and my mom called. "Hi, honey."

"Hi, Mom, what's new?"

"Well, your dad has a lump on his leg."

"WHAT!"

"He's going to see a doctor tomorrow, Ann."

"OK, Mom. It could be an infection or something else."

"Right, I don't know, but we'll wait and see."

A week passed and the test results came back. I called my mom.

"Mom, what did the doctors say?"

"It's non-Hodgkin's lymphoma, stage 4."

I was twenty-five years old. Now when the cancer bomb hits a family, it is horrible. All you can see is death. You are very ignorant about the whole situation. I was sure that we had very little time left with my dad. I wanted my dad to see my child before he left.

"Mat, I want to have a baby now before my dad dies."

"OK, Ann."

"This means we really have to work on it, Mat. You can't say you're tired or put me off."

"I will try, Ann."

Mat and I tried for six months and nothing. I started to think maybe I couldn't conceive a child for some reason, but I woke up one day and started bleeding out of nowhere. Jean convinced me to go to the doctor. The doctor examined me and said, "You're going to be a mother." The feeling that comes over you at that point is amazing.

She came back in the room and said something was very wrong.

"What is wrong?" I ask.

"The baby may abort itself at this time. We won't know for a couple of days."

"What can I do to keep my baby safe?"

"Ann, there is nothing you can do. This is in God's hands now. Go home and rest."

Mat was out of town, and I was all alone. Beth came and spent the night with me so I wasn't alone. That night I miscarried our first child. What a horrid, empty feeling.

Mat returned the next day. He felt bad, but nothing—no kiss, no anything. I felt so alone.

My mom understood how I was feeling. She just prayed for me. One month later, I was pregnant again. We all needed some good news with my dad's cancer and my miscarriage. This brought smiles to everyone's face.

I had a very rough pregnancy. I was sick from the moment I conceived until the moment I gave birth. I worked all the way through. I would just excuse myself, go throw up, and come back and start working again. Another year with no intimacy and no touching, but I was so sick again it didn't matter much at that point. Mat just left me alone.

Our first child was born. He was beautiful. His name was Michael. My mom and dad came to the hospital and brought me yellowy-orange roses. I remember thinking, *I wish my husband would show his love for me somehow,* but nothing.

Michael grew into a little boy with sandy-brown hair and big brown eyes like his dad and nice full lips like his mom in his oval-shaped face. Life was busy, but it seemed like Mat had lost all interest in me. I found myself almost begging Mat to touch me in any way, but with no success. I was helping out with my dad as his illness grew worse.

Two years after Michael was born, Jean got married. We all stayed busy with the wedding. I was the maid of honor, and I threw the rehearsal dinner at my house. My dad was starting to wear down from all the chemo he had to take and nothing was stopping the cancer, so the wedding was an uplifting event for everyone. The wedding was fun, and we all had a little too much to drink. Mat left early to go pick up Michael, and I was to follow. We all went back to my mom and dad's house where all of our personal belongings were. Everything was thrown in a back bedroom and a mess. The best man and I were back in the room, trying to find our stuff in the dark because my dad was in bed already. A little drunk and giggly, we were trying to be quiet. He pulled me over and started kissing me. Wow! Was that what a kiss was supposed to feel like? Mat never kissed me like that. I pushed back and looked into his eyes with passion, still I walked away because I was married, and I did not want to cross that line. I went home and cried all the way. A week later I told Jean about it. She knew Mat was never great or even good with touching me at all. I think something snapped in me that day. I was so down, which just wasn't me. I wasn't feeling very good about myself, my life, my marriage. My thirtieth birthday was just around the corner. I sat down with Mat two days later; I was very angry.

"Mat, I cannot do this anymore."

"Do what, Ann?"

"I cannot beg you to love me. What is wrong with me? Am I too fat or not pretty enough? What is it?"

*Total silence…*yet tears welled up in Mat's eyes.

I calmed down, and I said very firmly, "I can't even divorce you, Mat! I have a two-year-old, my father is dying, and I cannot bring any more upon my mother's head right now. We have no money, and I have nowhere to go. I'm going away for a week for my birthday alone, Mat. I need to remember who I am!"

Mat never said a word. He just stared at me.

For the next few months I started to take care of me for a change. I lost weight, and I was running six days a week. I was looking as fine as wine. I met up with a few friends on the East Coast and ran with the wind in my hair. Men were paying attention to me, and I began to feel like a woman. But in my mind, I was married, and I was not the fool-around kind of girl. I was very Catholic. When I got home, I had a renewed spirit. Mat was a little cold to me when I returned, but I was still really angry with him. Our tenth wedding anniversary was in a few weeks, and I had set up a nice night out at a really nice hotel for us almost ten months ago. Now I really didn't want to go. A friend of mine worked there and had made all kinds of special arrangements just for us. I wasn't going to be rude or unthoughtful. She did all this for me. So I had to go and put a smile on my face. Mat was on his best behavior because he knew how mad I was with him. When we got there, the room was all set up with chocolate-covered strawberries and champagne in an ice bucket. It was all very romantic, but I didn't even want him to touch me.

"Ann, don't you even want to make love tonight for our ten years together?"

"No, Mat. First of all, I'm on my period, and second, I don't want to do anything with you tonight. I'm tired, and I want to go to bed."

It was a sad evening. One week later, Mat was really trying to patch things up with me. "Come on, Ann, let's make love for our tenth anniversary."

I looked at Mat that night, and I thought he was really trying so I went along. We made love, if that's what you would call it.

CHAPTER 2

My Father's Last Days

ONE MONTH LATER MY COUSIN was getting married out of state. I was going with my mom, dad, and sister Beth. Mat was staying home with Michael because he was too little to bring. We were staying with my Aunt Flo. I went for a run to unwind from the long trip. When I got back, all the women were sitting around talking. My aunt Flo was saying she went to see a fortune-teller. I never put much merit into these people, but she did. She told us what they told her. She said that two women in the family were pregnant, and they were both having girls!

I started to laugh. "Don't look at me!"

My sister Jean was pregnant and having a girl, but who else could it be? No matter, we were going to the wedding, and I went to get dressed. I looked very svelte that night. I was surprised at the reaction from everyone. It was as if a beautiful movie star had walked into the room. Beth was jealous—she is a greedy person who can be very mean—and made a comment about how I looked. I was alone and had no husband to get my drinks from the bar, so I had to go myself. Men of all ages approached me that night. I knew I was a married woman, but I was having fun dancing and all the attention was great for my self-esteem. Finally my dad came to the dance floor and saved me from all the wild men that night. Even when they asked me to dance after that, I said I was already dancing with my best man, my dad. My dad and I danced until his suit coat was wet with sweat. Surely a night to remember!

We returned home, and Mat was still cold but I didn't care. I kissed my little boy Michael and carried on. The following week I was running before work, and it was hot out. I stopped in the middle of my run to throw up. I felt like the heat had gotten to me, so I stopped and went home. The next day it was cooler, so I was running again. Halfway through, I got sick again and all of a sudden I thought, *Oh my god, am I pregnant? Did my Aunt Flo's words come true? Am I the other woman in my family to have a baby?* I went out and got a home pregnancy test. I did not want to be pregnant. Not now. I was just finding myself again. I watched the test light up positive and I thought wow, I'm going to be a mom again. I called my mom and dad to tell them about the new grandchild that was on its way. I called Mat but I did not tell him on the phone. I met him for dinner, which was a rare occasion for us to go out, and I told him after we were done. He was very excited with the news of another child, but the thought of going through another pregnancy and how sick I got was not pleasant.

A few weeks passed when my mom called with the bad news. "Your father's cancer is turning for the worst." It was the impending doom that had hung over our family for four and a half years now. My dad had fought a good fight but was starting to lose now. I was feeling the sickness of my pregnancy in full swing now. I could no longer run because I had started to spot, and the doctor said, "No running, no nothing, or you are going to lose the baby." My dad needed a lot of care, and I was helping my mother a lot. Taking off a lot of work, gone from home, Mat never said a word. He knew I had to help my parents.

I was seven months pregnant, and my dad was really bad. I remember picking him up from the hospital the last time. We sat in my car. I had sunglasses on because I didn't want him to see me crying. He said to me, "I'm tired, and I don't want to try anymore." I couldn't even speak at that point. I was hiding my tears, but I knew it was going to be over soon. My dad re-entered the hospital a week later. My mother never left his side. I was there a lot of the time, and I hadn't slept in forty-eight hours. I was starting to have contractions, and I knew it was too early for that. I left the hospital at 10:00 p.m. that night. I told my mom I would return in the morning at 9:00 a.m. My father passed away at 6:30 a.m. before I could return.

My marriage was put on the back burner for a while. The funeral was long, and my whole family was in a dark place. My mother was so distraught with mourning his death. There was no joy at all to be found. My dad never saw my baby, but I think he held her in heaven until she was born. Two months after my dad's death, my daughter Grace was born. I was the other woman in the family that my aunt Flo spoke of. When they announced that I had a girl in the delivery room, tears ran down my face. I whispered softly, "It's a girl, Dad."

In the weeks after Grace was born, my mother became very depressed. Grace's birth was a big bright spot in her life. It was a very hot summer, and we didn't have air-conditioning. My mom called every day for a week. "Ann, bring that baby over here and stay with me for a while. It's too hot for her." I knew that she needed me to come because she didn't know how to carry on without my dad yet. Mat and I packed up the kids and the dog and went to live with my mom for the next eight weeks. Every morning my mom would get up with Grace so I could sleep a little. Mat was off to work, and he would take Michael to day care. I could hear my mom on the phone with her sister, telling her how the baby smiles at her and how the baby knows her already. It was nice to hear her have some joy in her voice again. The eight weeks flew by, and it was time to leave and go home. My mom came to me and said, "Ann, thank you, honey. I couldn't have gotten through this without you."

"Mom, you're going to be fine."

For the next five years I was busy raising kids and helping my mom with the mountain of paperwork after my dad's death. My sisters were all busy with their jobs, so I was the one who had the most adjustable schedule. I had very little time to think about Mat never touching me at all since Grace was conceived.

It was time for Grace to go to school, her first day at kindergarten. I felt my mom should come to see her off since she and Grace had a special bond. Grace was the apple of my mom's eye. Grace was a beautiful child with chestnut-brown hair and chocolate-brown eyes, big curly eyelashes, and a little round face with pink cheeks. My mom told me once, "Ann, you know Grace is my favorite, but let's keep that between me and you so there are no hurt feelings."

"I know, Mom, you're not fooling me."

CHAPTER 3

Trying to Fix Things

IT WAS NOW SEVEN YEARS after my dad's death, and it was time to work on my marriage again.

Mat came into the kitchen where I was working on dinner. I was so starved for love and affection from him. I stopped him as he walked through. I gently backed him up against the counter. "Mat, you are going to kiss me. Put your arms around me and kiss me!"

Reluctantly, he did. He was as stiff as aboard, and I should have just kissed a tree. It would have had more feeling in it. I knew I had gained weight with Grace's birth, and I was still carrying it, but I wasn't five hundred pounds with flies buzzing around me either. "Mat, was that so hard?"

He just walked away.

I followed him. "I am your wife, Mat. Am I too fat, too ugly, what is it?"

He just left.

I tried for a while to be a wife; but life becomes busy with two kids, homework, sports, birthday parties, my mom and her needs, my housework, going to work, etc.

Seven more years flew by. Grace was in middle school and Michael in high school. It was lonely along the way. I prayed all the time. *God, I have promised to love him, but he won't be a husband to me.* When I started to think about our relationship, what could I really fault him on? He was a good dad for the most part. He brought a steady paycheck; even if it wasn't huge, it paid the bills. He took care of half of the housework. He didn't hit me or do drugs or even drink that much. He was home every night. We never argued unless it was about loving me. OK, now I sounded like a whiny baby. *I'm sorry, God,* I thought, *now I will shut up. And if this is how you want me to live, then I will.* I must be too fat, too ugly, too something.

I found other ways to be loved. Hugs and kisses from my children. I always had dogs; it's amazing how a dog loves all the time. Friends, family, my mom, and more. I just started to close that other part of me down. It was much easier to close it down than be rejected all the time. You just keep going.

Mat came home one day and told me he had lost his job. We barely made enough to cover the bills, and I knew we had to cut our losses. "Mat, we have to sell the house and move to an area where our money can go further for us."

"Ann, what are you talking about?"

"Look, Mat, I don't know how long we can hold out with these bills, and a house just doesn't sell overnight. So we have to start now before we don't have anything left. I'll take care of it. Mat, you just look for a job."

CHAPTER 4

The Move

SELLING THE HOUSE WAS SO stressful for the whole family. Michael was in his senior year of high school, and he didn't want to leave. I understood but what could we do? Grace was just finding herself, and it was going to be hardest on her. I was going to be there for her though.

I knew I would probably be moving from my mom, but I was a driver, and she could spend time at the house. All in all the house had to be sold, and we had to move on.

For the next year and a half, we tried to sell the house. What a chore! Trying to keep it clean all the time, dozens of people in and out looking through all your stuff, and the mounting pressure of the bills. Mat landed a job nine months later after we started to sell the house. We were struggling financially.

Michael graduated from high school and was entering his first year of college, and Grace was starting high school as a freshman when the house sold.

This accelerated life. I now had to find another place to live. I was on a mission. I found a house in our budget that was a bulldozer of a house, but I could look through the dirt and repairs that were needed and see a home for us. My mom came with me to look it. She was the kind of person who could take burlap and make satin. I trusted her totally.

"Well, Ann, there is a lot of work here, but I can see the possibilities here."

"That's all I needed, Mom."

We bought the house and had back-to-back closings. There was so much to do! Packing, packing, packing! I had to pull Grace out of the middle of her school year and start her in a new high school where everyone had already set their group of friends. Teenage girls aren't always the friendliest.

We had moved out of our home we sold, and we were spending the week with my mom before we move to our new home, which was a real fixer-upper. A home Mat and I bought for growing old together. Our son Michael was away at college for his freshman year and our daughter Grace was fourteen and a freshman in high school.

I was excited even though there was a lot of work to be done. Leaving the city life for a bit more country was going to be difficult. A lot more land and raw nature, how beautiful! I was so ready. I had so many plans going on in my head for the future. I really wanted to help Grace start in her new school, so I was going to pick her up twice a week for lunch until she felt more comfortable. This was in between work on the house. She was the hardest hit by the move. It was hard for her to leave all of her friends and start over. She's not very happy about the move.

CHAPTER 5

The Accident

IT WAS MY DAY OFF, and we were about to move from Mom's house to the new house. I was running around doing last-minute errands, and my sister Kathy called and asked if I could run to the mall for her. It's way out of my way, but I said yes. I was tired when I headed back to my mom's house. I was driving on State Road at 1:30 in the afternoon. I stopped to wait for the guy in front of me to move. He stopped in the left lane, and I waited patiently for him to move. It's taking too long, and I was trying to sound the horn. I stopped for about fifteen to twenty seconds when I was rear-ended by an Econoline van. Even though I had my seat belt on, the force of the impact was great and the left side of my face and body were jammed into the steering wheel and column. My head hit the steering wheel and my body crunched into a position that should not be. I thought, *Oh my god, I'm going to be brain dead in ten minutes*. I hit really hard. When my head came back up, I looked in the rearview mirror with my right eye and saw that I need an ambulance. I used the OnStar button to call for help. Next I saw traffic in front of me, and I thought I better get out of the car. I took off my seat belt and opened the car door. The man who hit me was there. He said he was sorry and that it was his fault and told me, "Please pull your car out of the traffic."

I couldn't see very well, but I was afraid of being hit again. I started the car and pulled in a JiffyLube parking lot and parked the car. OnStar came back on the line and told me help was on the way. They asked if they should stay on the line with me, but I said, "No, thank you." I called my mother to tell her of the accident. She lived very close and she could call Mat for me. Once more I opened the car door to get out. I stood up and felt like I was going to be sick. I sat back down in the car. The man who hit me was there again. He was very shook up. "Oh my god!" he kept saying.

I could not see out of my left eye, and blood was running down my face. My body was hurting, but my head hurt the worst. The police arrived and told me not to move. The fire department came and started checking my neck and back and decided to use a neck brace and back board. I was put into an ambulance and taken to the hospital.

I was scared as we arrived at the hospital. I could hear Mat talking. As the doctors came in, so did Mat. All I want him to do was hold my hand and comfort me, but he took a seat at the foot of the bed, and I couldn't even see him. I felt so alone.

The doctors had to pry open my eye with a surgical tool to look at it. It hurt so bad.

In the ER, I was taken for several x-rays of my back and neck. My eye was in a great deal of pain. They stained it and numbed it to look at the damage. I was told that the whole cornea was gone and to see an ophthalmologist as soon as possible. They wanted to stitch up the cuts on my face, but they were very close to my eye and I said no.

A friend of mine was a cardiologist on staff there. His name was Bart Joeby. I asked a nurse, "Nurse, would you please see if Dr. Joeby is in today? And if he is, would you please call him to the ER?"

"Sure, it will be a few minutes though."

"OK."

Thoughts ware running through my head. Mat was sitting at the end of my bed and all I really wanted was for him to come and hold my hand or kiss me and tell me everything's all right. He talked to me, but I couldn't even see him. He didn't even touch me at all. I guess it's nothing new for he has not touched me for years. Still I felt very alone right now.

Finally Bart showed up.

"Ann, oh my god, how are you doing?"

"Hi, Bart. Come on over the top of me so I can see you. How bad does it look?"

"Pretty bad, Ann. With a head trauma like that, you need a CAT scan. I'm pretty sure that will be tomorrow. I'll check on my way out. Ann, I have to get back upstairs."

"Thanks for coming down, Bart."

They released me and told me to see an ophthalmologist very soon. I was sent home on Vicodin, which made me sick to my stomach and a little out of it, 800 mg ibuprofen, and Flexeril. I took a Vicodin, but it made me very ill.

Mat took me to my mother's house because we hadn't really moved into our new one. She was sick with worry. She comforted me like any good mother would do. She made me some food and told me to sleep in her bed. She kept everything quiet. It's just what I needed. My cell phone rang, and it's an insurance adjuster for the man who hit me. He knew I was really hurt bad and was trying to trick me into saying I was all right. I told him I was all drugged up and cannot talk right now and hung up. I knew at this point I needed a lawyer. I told Mat and he said, "NO LAWYERS." I told him that I was really hurt bad, and I was going to need help.

I didn't know anything about insurance, and we had no choice. We were people who didn't have a lot and again I was going to need help. I was very firm when I told Mat that I was getting a lawyer.

I slept for the rest of the night.

At 8:30 a.m., I was in the ophthalmologist's office. Dr. Samuel Kozlow had to pry open my eye, just like they did in the hospital, because it was so badly swollen shut and very bruised. My back, neck, hip, and knee were in pain on the left side, but my eye needed the quickest care. Dr. Kozlow numbed my eye because of the intense pain. He held the eyelid open with a tool. My vision was very blurry. He told me the cornea was shaved off and he felt with such a hard blow to the head there was a lot more damage that we couldn't see. He sent me for a CAT scan and sure enough it's way worse. The ocular floor of the bone under my eye was gone. The nerves that were around the eye were hooked up on the jagged edge of the piece of bone that was left. All the tissue that was around the eye had fallen into my sinus cavity, and my eye was sinking very fast, along with the cornea being shaved off. The fifth cranial nerve that was located just under the left eye had been smashed and damaged as well. When your body is in so much pain and so torn up, one pain will take over, and right now it's my eye. He sent me home with eye drops.

I kept both of my eyes closed all the time because of the pain. It was better to just stay in darkness. I had to see our family doctor, Dr. Henry Samson, today for the rest of my body. I was taking 800 mg ibuprofen to keep the pain down. My stomach was handling them for the moment. The headaches were so bad, I wanted to hit my head on the wall to relieve the pain.

I didn't feel strong enough on my feet to take the Flexeril. I was blind 98 percent of the time, and it was hard to get around. Dr. Samson said no therapy for a week and wrote another four scrips for pain. I needed to lie down and rest. We were supposed to move to our new home. We cannot for now.

The next morning, my eyes were very sensitive to light even though they were shut all of the time. Everyone shut the lights off for me. It was 7:30 a.m. and I was getting the CAT scan of my eye. I was taking 800 mg ibuprofen every six hours, but it was starting to take its toll on my stomach. I'm glad my mother was here to help. I'm still in a lot of pain. I wish I could go to my new home. There was so much work to be done. I lay low today. My back, neck, leg, and stomach were bad today. I took pain meds and kept my eyes closed. I've been living in a world of darkness for almost a week now.

I'm a hairstylist, and my clients were starting to leave. I'm afraid that when I get back to work, no one will be left.

Two days later, Mat and I had an appointment with a lawyer that morning. I looked so bad, but I don't even care. It hurt just to move. Mat was there but not much help. I had never had to hire a lawyer of this type, so I'm really not sure how to proceed, but I know it's necessary. His name is Kyle Wilcox. He explained a lot and had me sign a contract with him for his fees. Mat cannot take any more time off work to drive me around to doctor appointments so the insurance company sent a driver for me because I cannot see. Insurance is a tricky thing, and the lawyer was helpful in telling me how to use it to take care of me. He told me what the insurance will pay for to help me recover, not only for doctors and medication, but also things like someone to clean the house and drive me to appointments. I didn't know any of this.

Later in the day, I was back in the ophthalmologist's office to go over the results of the CAT scan. The swelling was down, and he could see my eye was better. He told me that I had to see a surgeon, but asked where I wanted to go. My eyes were always like a hawk's eyes. Perfect! Never did I have a problem with them, so this was all new territory for me. I told him I wanted to go to a well-known university eye center. From what I know, they are the best. It was hard to get an appointment, but they got me in because you only have two weeks from the time of injury since scar tissue builds up, so time is of the essence. The double vision and pain concerned him. He told me that it must be done soon or there will be too much scar tissue. He referred me to a specialist in eye surgery, Dr. Christine Nelson. The appointment was made for tomorrow morning.

It was 6:20 a.m., and there was a huge snowstorm going on right now. The kind of storm you just want to stay home in, but I had to go to Dr. Nelson. The insurance company was sending a driver to pick me up. I brought a pillow for my back and leg. My face on the left had been numb since the accident. I kept burning my throat and mouth because I couldn't feel my teeth. I had been examined now for two hours. My eyes hurt, my face hurts. The doctor knew that time is of the essence, but the CAT scan that I had brought on disc cannot be read with their equipment, so she said I needed to come back tomorrow with the hard pictures of the CAT scan to make a decision regarding surgery. She wanted to reexamine me because the swelling was going down a little. It had been a long and painful day. I couldn't take ibuprofen any longer in case we go into surgery. I tried to sleep.

The driver picked me up at 12:30 p.m. for my next appointment. The weather was better, but very sunny, and hurt my eyes, even with dark sunglasses on. I felt like a vampire when the sun came up. The double vision made me sick to my stomach. My eyes kept trying to focus just like a camera, but they could not. It drove me crazy after a little bit. I was reexamined for two hours again. I had brought the hard copy pictures of the CAT scan today. Our time window for surgery was getting short. The doctor showed me the scans, and I began to understand how bad my injuries were. The doctor scheduled surgery in two days. I do believe she could help, but I was afraid to go to surgery. No real pain meds— only extra-strength Tylenol. It's not strong enough, but it helped. Grace was left without help getting started at her new school, and there was so much work to be done at the new house that I could not do now.

The doctor told me to see if my eyesight would improve any before surgery, but today, I don't see any change. Still very blurry and the double vision almost seemed worse. The numbness in my face had not gotten any better. The doctor told me surgery would make it worse. We had to move soon. I could not help Grace get settled in her new high school. I felt like a bad mother.

I tried to put the pain out of my mind, but the headaches were bad. The longer I was out of my work cutting hair, the chances of going back grew slim. Money was becoming very tight.

The day before surgery, I wanted to go to church and move to my own house. I didn't know if I could take care of myself but I'll try. I didn't feel well at all. I hate to miss church, but I was too weak. I wanted to help Grace get settled in her new school, but I could not drive, and I was on too many drugs.

I was still living in my mom's house, but we moved all our clothes and furniture to the new house a week ago. My family was in limbo. We were living out of a suitcase. Grace needed to start school, and I was heading into surgery. I had to make some decisions. Mat and I decided we had to move and leave my mom's house. I sat down with my mom and thanked her for taking such good care of all of us, but it was time to move. We finally said good-bye to Mom and left for our new home. We moved to the new house the day before I had to go into surgery. What a mess it was, but I was excited to start working on the house even in pain!

CHAPTER 6

The Surgery

WE'RE IN OUR OWN HOUSE now, and I was anxious about tomorrow's surgery. The vision was still bad so I must go through with the surgery if I hope to get better. I hate people playing with my eyes. I've never had to deal with that. I've always had twenty-twenty vision. The house was a mess. Boxes were everywhere. Everything you touched was dirty. The bathrooms were torn apart. Mice and bugs infested the house.

It's hard to get around by myself. There was no one to help.

My cornea was starting to repair itself a little. They told me that in surgery it would be redamaged from the tools they used because they work so close to the eyeball itself, and the fifth cranial nerve will be resmashed some too. I really had no choice because my eye was sinking fast, and my vision was off. I was still seeing double and the wrong colors too.

It's 8:00 a.m., and they were prepping me for surgery. I really didn't feel well, and my blood pressure was up. I just wanted to get this over. Grace was in the ninth grade and starting her brand-new school out here. I was hoping to ease her in school and be there for her, but I'm heading into surgery. I had no choice. She was panicking. "Mom, I don't know anyone. What do I do?"

I told her, "Honey, go in and introduce yourself to the counselor and tell her the situation. She will help you." I felt so bad leaving her there alone. I wanted this to be a good experience for her. My hands were tied, and I needed to stay calm for surgery.

They were getting me ready now, and I'm very uncomfortable. I had them stuff pillows under my knees so I didn't lay the wrong way when I'm under anesthesia and wake up any worse.

Surgery was over, and they pumped a lot of pain meds and anti-nausea meds into me. My eye was swollen shut again. In surgery, the cornea was redamaged, and I'm blind again for about two more weeks. Back to a world of darkness. I was put on Tylenol with codeine for pain. They wanted me to sleep at home and come back in two days for a check.

The fracture was a good size and in a thicker point of the bone—very unusual. The tissue from the eye was caught on the bone, and they had to repack my eye tissue and repair the bottom floor plate of my eye. I was very drugged up and sent home. Grace was left to fend for herself in her new school.

When I came home that night my mom called. "How are you feeling? I should have come to help you," she said, but we now live more than an hour apart. My mom's a real homebody and was not comfortable outside of her home for very long. Still, talking with her brought me comfort.

It felt like day one of the crash all over again. I was not out of the drug fog yet. The Tylenol with codeine at least let me sleep.

I woke up the next morning alone and blind. I had to sleep sitting up so my eye would not swell. There was someone working on ripping the house apart. Mat left for work, and Grace was going back to the school where she was so out of place. She hated it there. I was trying to come out of the drug fog that I'm in just to walk. My body was all torn up from the accident, but I had to let my eye heal. I was afraid that I would lose vision. I had to be careful.

Three days later, a new driver picked me up for an after-surgery check for my eye. I really didn't want to go. I didn't feel well at all. It's sunny out, and it killed my eyes even though they were closed. They had to examine my eye, and it hurt so much I passed out twice. It's not good to touch it yet. My face was numb from my left ear to the middle of my nose. I could not feel several of my teeth or part of the roof of my mouth. They told me to go home and just rest. I would see them in a week. It's hard because I always had to go alone.

The next day, the pain was not good, probably because of yesterday's appointment, and the Tylenol with codeine had taken its toll. I could not go to the bathroom, and my stomach did not feel well. I had to switch to regular Tylenol again; it helped but not real well. I just slept a lot today to try to keep the pain down. I was worried about Grace at school. I was locked in the house alone.

I had to pry my eye open to put in medicine. This alone made me sick. I was seeing double again and the wrong colors. This scared me. I tried to open my eye here and there through the day. I tire very easily; I get stabbing pain all the time in my eye now. It would be a long time before I could return to work. I feel I may lose my job.

The swelling from surgery was going down a bit. I could open my eye about three-quarters of the way. I was still seeing double, and my eye really burned. My face was still numb. There was much work to be done in the house, and I couldn't do anything, even cooking dinner was out. When Mat and Grace came home, they do what they can to cook in this mess of what's left of the kitchen.

My doctors told me the burning in my face was the nerve trying to come alive. For the next six weeks, no lifting or pressure should be put on my eye. I had to sleep sitting up to keep the swelling down. I had no way of getting around without driving. Money was getting very tight; my boss was not happy about me being away for so long.

I needed groceries. The store had someone put them in the car for me, but I couldn't carry them in the house. They had to sit outside till someone came home.

CHAPTER 7

Getting Better

I STARTED PHYSICAL THERAPY; MAYBE they could help. It's been about four months since the surgery. Grace had a concert at school that night. I went for her. I felt so bad, but I could not disappoint her again. I was just not able to be there for her most of the time.

I could open my eyes, but I was still healing. Grace hated her new school. She had no friends yet, and every day she came home and she told me how much she hated it! I wanted to help her, but I was on so much medication that I was drugged all the time. I wanted to meet her for lunch, pick her up early, even take a day off with her, but I just dragged from the pain and drugs.

I was trying to sleep and my whole head and body hurt. I was back in the same bed with Mat because I didn't have to sit up and sleep anymore. He rolled over and punched me in the eye. The pain was tremendous, and he said he's sorry but somehow I don't feel it was an accident. I just let it go.

My eye surgeon told me today that I would have double vision for the rest of my life now. My eye was damaged too much and not repairable. It was a bit of a handicap, but I was really glad I could see. I just had to learn to live with it; like someone who loses an arm or a leg. Could I still stand all day and cut hair? I don't know yet.

Spring was here, and I was not even walking right. I needed to find a doctor to help me with the rest of my injuries because the therapy didn't work. The therapist had me walk in water on a treadmill and put me on some arm exercises to start. Soon she quit her job there, and I was kind of left on my own. A massage therapist tried to help, but I couldn't even lie down yet. Nothing they did made me feel better.

The house was shredded. Dirt, boxes, ripped-out walls, no flooring, and mice were everywhere. You could hear them in the walls at night. I'm in so much pain I didn't even care. Grace was having such a hard time fitting in at school. I fear it's taking her to a dark place. I have tried to meet her for lunch a few times, and it seemed to help her get through the day, but it's hard for me because I was still on so much medication. Mat was now staying with my mom for a few days each week. She's close to his work, and the winter weather had been really dangerous.

I found a local doctor to look at the rest of my injuries from the accident. I was very protective of my eye and face right now; but my neck, back, and hip were all sore. The doctor didn't really know what to do with me, so he sent me to a specialist who deals with car-accident victims. While I was between doctors, I tried to start my own therapy by just going to the community indoor pool and slowly walking in the water. It really was hard on my eyes. It's amazing how the pressure of the water affected them. The doctor told me to stop immediately. I was sent to hands-on therapy and physical rehab.

My pain levels were way too high. I stood in my kitchen with a heat pack on my head just trying to get the pain of my body in control. My back had a swelling on the left side under my shoulder blade, the size of an ostrich egg, and my spine burned like it's on fire. Hoping for some help, I started physical therapy with a new team of people. I think they just were afraid to touch me for fear they're going to hurt me more. I would let no one touch my face, but my back and left hip needed help. There was a u-pick orchard close to the house, and I kept trying to help myself by picking blueberries just to move my arms. They kept going numb, and my body was twisting funny. The car insurance was on my back to do more. My mom called me every day! "How are you feeling, honey?" I don't get to see her as much as I would like to. I'm very close to my mom.

I was not really happy with the way my therapy was going. I seemed to be getting worse. I was trying to keep track of all the medical bills for the insurance company and myself, so I went and asked for copies of the services and charges from therapy. They gave me this stack of papers, and

I was like, "Wow, I'm really high maintenance." I started to read them just to find I had been billed for services never done; false charges billed to my car insurance. I was being ripped off and getting bad care. I was often left alone in the pool by myself! I was done with this place but still in so much pain. I went to the insurance company and told them, but nothing was done.

I prayed to God and thanked Him for all he had given me and also to help me find someone to help me heal.

My body was getting worse. I couldn't even stand up and my shoulders were twisted. I went back to the local doctor. I told him I needed some way to move muscles in my back. My head pain was too high, and I was not walking well. He pulled out five business cards and told me that all of these places offer massage to try to help me. I said, "Well, give me this one," as I grabbed the far-right card; I had to start somewhere.

Mat's father had Alzheimer's disease, and he was getting bad, so Mat tried to go see him once or twice a week. Between work and working in the house, there's not a whole lot of time left. Grace was starting tenth grade, and she just hated the new school! Teachers were not helpful, she had no real friends, and a boy was bullying her around. She knew I'm in pain and tried not to complain, but sometimes it just poured out of her. I was trying to be there for her. She went to work with her father a lot to help out. Michael was back at college this year for his sophomore year. He worked out of state this summer to make some tuition money and helped a little with the house before he went back. It felt like the family was settling down, and the house was coming along but still a long way to go. Money was tight and my boss kept calling to ask when I could return to work. I told her that I didn't know if I could return yet at all. The house was costing more than we planned. We owned it free and clear for a short time, but we had to take out a mortgage to pay for the work. It's only put in Mat's name because I was not working and that would hurt the application.

As Mat's father got worse, Mat and Grace kept going to help. She was always such a good kid, but I saw her becoming withdrawn.

The Thanksgiving holiday was coming soon, and my mom always gathers us for the holidays. She is such a great mom! All my sisters come with their families and even though it's loud and the workload is a lot, my mother always does the most for all of us.

I was hoping the holidays would cheer Grace up. Michael would be home and maybe there would be some nice family time.

I was starting a new treatment today with a massage therapist. It's in a pain management clinic. I have never been to this kind of clinic before nor do I want to go to one, but I needed the massage. I was beginning to think that there was no one to help me. I kept praying to God to send someone to help, but I thanked him for all he does for me. As I entered the new office, I looked around and a big black Lab came up to me. I thought, *How weird is this, a dog in a doctor's office.* I heard the staff call the dog by its name, which is Mango. I was not quite sure how I felt about it, but I am a dog lover, so I think it's going to be OK. The receptionist told me that my insurance would cover seeing the doctor if I want. I said that I would not mind another opinion. The massage therapist came and took me back to her room, got me prepared and tried to work on me. She could hardly touch me because my back was so sore and swollen. She completed fifteen minutes of the hour she was supposed to do and stopped "The doctor will see you now," she told me. I was confused because I knew I needed more. I stepped over to see the doctor. He seemed young to me, but I guess I just feel old. He asked me about the accident. After a very brief talk, he asked me to stand and put my hands behind my head and locked my fingers together. I think he was testing some movement or something and then he moved my back. It felt like someone poured acid down my spine. Every nerve in my back was on fire. I fell to the floor in pain.

The doctor is a little afraid, I think. He said, "You are really bad."

My thoughts are *Really, ya think?*

"You need to come back tomorrow," he said.

I didn't know what to do, but I knew I needed help, so I came back the next day. Again he moved my back and the same thing happened. He said, "You are really bad, and you need to come back again tomorrow."

I was so discouraged and in pain. Should I go back? There was no one else to go to. I went home, praying all the way, "Please, God, help me."

I went back the next day, and the doctor came in and he started to move me, but this time I said, "No!"

"What hurts you?" he asked.

"Everything except my lips," I said back, and at that moment, I meant it.

He didn't know what to do. He called his partner to come and look at me because he just didn't know what to do.

It's funny when these odd feelings pour over your body and you know something is about to change. It's like God is saying, "It's going to be OK. I'm right here!" The second therapist walked into the room and something just told me this man was going to be special in my life, but how? *Is he the one that is going to help me out pain? Has he been sent by God to help me?*

I smile.

He said, "Now tell me about your accident. I need to know everything."

We went over the whole thing step by step. He was the only doctor to ask such detail about it. He looked at me and said, "I've seen people like you before, and if you don't get aggressive with your treatment, you will lock into the wrong position forever."

I said, "Well, no one else has a plan, so what do you have in mind?"

"Your treatment will be six days a week, two to three hours a day. We have to strip your muscles and move you every day."

I said, "Well, let's begin tomorrow."

I knew I was about to go through some big pain. I went home and told Mat about it, and he said, "Go for it." He was still going back and forth with his dad, so I was on my own.

We started the next day with just about everything— massage, heat, electric stimulation, and adjustments. Every day I had to strip down to my waist, and they worked on my back. I knew I had to relax so they could do their job, but how? This was not only painful but embarrassing. I went to the older doctor and said, "I have a very short time with you because the insurance company is going to cut me off, so we need to work fast. First, I know my injuries are not your average ones, so there are only two or three of you who have the experience and skills I need. Second, I'm going to be here a lot, so we need to be on a first-name basis so I can relax and get comfortable. And third, we're going to need a stick for me to bite on to help me through the pain."

We all laughed but they agreed. I didn't call them "doctor" anymore, but they were Larry, who is the older of the two, and Allen now.

I spent a lot of time with Larry and Allen, and we all got to know each other well. You just get comfortable and you talk. They came in on their days off just to take care of me even on the holidays. Larry was closer to my age, and he and I could talk well together. He was about five foot six, in good shape, with silver hair and blue eyes. He was the one that I knew would help me. He tried to get me to relax so he could work on my back, but it was painful. He would get me to talk about anything just to distract me.

"So are you married?"

"Yes," I answered.

"How long?"

"Too long," I said. "How about you?"

"Forever."

We both laughed a little.

"I'm sure your husband is finding this hard not to be able to touch you."

I grew kind of sad and answered, "My husband is not like that. He really doesn't touch me at all. I'm not pretty enough, and I guess I'm too fat." I knew I was fifty pounds overweight.

Larry stopped what he's doing and looked at me. He said, "My wife is the same way with me, but I'm a man, and I will tell you it's not you."

"Well, Larry, I'm a woman, and it's not you either!"

Over the next few weeks, Larry and I shared a lot of personal stories about our lives. It seemed as if our lives mirror each other. We were both living a life of rejection from our spouses. We understood each other's pain because it was our own pain that we had become accustomed to living with, as if it were normal.

I asked Larry one day, "If it's not me, then what is it?"

"I don't know. You'll have to find that answer on your own."

"Larry," I said, "who sent you? God or the devil?"

"God," he answered, but I am not sure. I just know I have that odd feeling again.

Larry and I were talking more and more about our lives and trying to figure it out. I kept asking him, "Who sent you?" There's something above coincidence about the whole thing. For a month now, Larry kept telling me, "It's not you," and I'm beginning to believe him. We continued to work on my back. My neck and hip were worse, it seemed.

Christmas Day and Larry made me come in for therapy. "We can't lose ground with you right now," he told me. "I put you back, and the next day you're a mess again. We have to keep working at it!"

Mat's father was really bad now, so Mat tried to get to see him a few times a week; but for Christmas Day, we went to my mom's. Larry told me I had to do more to straighten my back by working out at a gym. I told Mat I was really going to be pushing hard. I was tired of being in pain.

The phone call came this morning announcing my father-in-law's death. The next few days were taken up with the funeral, and we had the whole family come back to our house to comfort each other. It was a good place for everyone to gather. The house was coming along, but there was still a lot to be done. I went to therapy through all of this. Larry and I talked more and more.

My brother-in-law John was staying with us to prepare for the funeral. He and Mat got into a fight over something small and Mat left. I looked at John and said, "He's always like this. Mad at the world and I don't know why."

John answered, "He wasn't always like this. He turned this way the day after our mother died when he was thirteen. He is stuck in the past. I so wanted to be close with him but he has never been a brother to me."

Now I've always liked John but never really opened up to him about our lives but that is about to change. "Well," I said, "don't feel bad because he has not touched me in many, many years."

John was stunned. "What do you mean? He's being a bad husband to you. You must be a saint to stay and put up with that." He looked at a picture of me that was sitting on the table. "Look at this picture of you. You're gorgeous in this picture. I guess you married the wrong brother!"

I was not in a laughing mood, but I did smile. John started me thinking. It's like putting pieces of a puzzle together.

The next day I returned to therapy and Larry was there. He came in, and I burst into tears. He held me for a minute, and I calmed down. He understood my pain because he lived it too.

Larry started to do his own questioning at his house and tried to unwrap his own life's mess. He and his wife had been through a lot of therapy in their marriage but didn't seem to be any closer to an answer as to what's wrong or how to fix anything. I was now starting to believe that he was not sent for me but that we were sent for each other.

My boss called and asked me when I was coming back to work. I couldn't give her an answer. She told me she had to let me go because she could no longer hold my position. Was this legal? Could she do that? I called my lawyer Kyle, and he said it happens all the time in these situations. We would have to sue for lost wages. I don't know anything about that, but I did nothing wrong. How could they do that!

CHAPTER 8

The Betrayal

I HAD THERAPY ONE JANUARY morning, and Larry and I were talking. Once again, it's not you, he said.

"Well, then what is it?"

"You have to find that out yourself," he told me.

"OK, then, I will."

I went home and asked Mat to sit down. "I want to talk with you."

How do I start this conversation? I was thinking. Well, I guess you just start. "Don't you think something is wrong with our marriage?" I said to him. "We live like brother and sister. You never touch me, and you haven't for years."

He said back to me, "Well, let's go have sex right now."

"What! I'm not even sure what I have left in that area. It's been so long."

He started acting a little weird and came back with, "Well, I guess we need a divorce, and we'll have to sell this house."

"Stop!" I said. "We have gone from why won't you touch me to getting a divorce and selling the house in five minutes. All I want is the truth. Are you gay?"

Most men would call you everything nasty they could think of if you say this to them, but his answer is different. "No, I'm not gay. I don't think I'm gay."

I was smelling a rat now, but still I went on. "All I want is the truth, and I'm giving you the chance to tell me. You know it. I will go the depths of hell to find the truth."

He said, "OK."

Grace was in the house and knew none of what was going on and I did not want to drag her into this. She was having a hard enough time at school already. So we cut the conversation short.

The next day I started my search by talking to family and friends that know us well. I opened up details of our life together and asked what they thought. I started with my mom.

"What do you think, Mom?"

"Honey, I've never had such problems in my marriage. I don't know what to tell you." She wanted to help me but she couldn't.

I needed to be alone with God so I went to the tabernacle at church and just talked with God. "Father in heaven, you know everything! I have honored my wedding vows, and I have been a good wife. Could this man have betrayed me this deep? Please show me the truth so I can see what I'm dealing with. I cannot condemn him for lying to me or betraying me or make a decision until I know the truth. Please help me, Father. Please!"

The more people I talked to, the more I felt like a fool. My sister Kathy said to me, "I thought he was gay the minute you married him."

My sister Beth did not believe any of it, and I still had no proof. I was losing weight rapidly and exercising a lot to rebuild myself but also to keep the stress down. I needed to go to Grace's school today because her swim coach was giving her problems. I was still on a lot of drugs and in pain, but I had to give her the strength to stand up for herself. She was really having a hard time with this new school.

Things were getting tense in the household, and I asked Mat to leave the bedroom until we figured things out. Here was a man I had loved and slept in the same bed with for twenty-seven years, and I felt like I was sleeping with a total stranger. He looked at me and said, "I'm not leaving my bedroom!"

I could be a smartass when I wanted. I turned and said, "I'm sorry, I thought you were the man!" It was hard to get into bed tonight.

I continued looking for answers from anywhere I can. I called my brother-in-law John and asked what he thinks. I was shocked to hear him say that Mat showed signs of being gay in high school. Why was this the first time I was hearing this? I was depending more and more on Larry to keep me sane. Sometimes he and I would talk for hours alone and just hold hands. I know that sounds stupid and childish, but when you are rejected all the time, something little like that is huge. Larry told me about a counselor who helped him and his wife at one time and he was local. We had no money because it is all going to the house, and I had no job. Mat's paycheck went to gas, food, bills, and very little was left over.

One day I went to see Larry, and he had left town for a week. I was lost. I needed someone to talk to now. I was losing it. I somehow got the courage to call this man Larry spoke of. The receptionist answered and said that it was his day off. She must have heard the desperation in my voice. "I only have fifteen minutes to wait," I said, "just forget I called."

"No, no, no," she said. "I'm going to try and get a hold of him, and I'll have him call you back."

"I only have fifteen minutes, and after that, forget it!"

"OK," she said.

I started to talk to God. "Fifteen minutes, that's all I have. If he doesn't call me, I will move on, but if You want me to talk to him, fifteen minutes is what I have."

As I waited for what seemed to be an eternity, ten minutes passed. "All right, I guess my head can just explode off my shoulders. I give!"

All of a sudden on the strike of the twelfth minute the phone rang. "Hello, is this Ann?"

My heart skipped a beat. "Yes, this is."

"This is Ken Meyers. I hear you want to talk to someone today."

"I don't have any money, but I need help."

"OK, Ann, can you come here at noon?"

"I'll be there, Ken. Thank you. I'll see you later."

As I hang up the phone, my whole body just tingled. We never think God is that close but he was right there this time.

I went about my morning with such anxiety. Still looking for answers about Mat, trying to keep it all from the kids. The house was wearing on me, and the tension was thick.

At noon, I arrived to see Ken. I was so nervous, and thoughts were running through my head. *Is he going to ask me to lie down on a couch? Is he going to fill my head with nonsense? Is he just going to be full of crap?* He stepped in to greet me.

"Hi, Ann. I'm Ken. Come in and sit, and we will talk." He was soft-spoken and fatherly. He seemed gentle and kind and honest.

I sat down and started to talk right away. "I don't even know why I'm here, but I feel like I'm going to explode soon."

"I don't know why you're here either, but I do know this, today is my day off but for some reason here I am."

Again that feeling walked over my whole body. Ken and I talked for about an hour and I told him my thoughts about Mat. He wanted to meet with Mat alone and then both of us together. I went home and sat Mat down and asked if he would like to try counseling. He was still holding his story up that he was not gay. I really had nothing to fault him on. He was home on time every night. He helped with half of the chores. He went to work every day, didn't drink or hang out with the guys; we had never argued about money. The only problem was touching me and this underlying anger he had always had. He said OK. Ken had set the meeting up for one week later and agreed to see us for free. I was grateful because things were tight. There was no room for anything extra and barely enough just to pay the bills.

The week was rolling on. I was in and out of doctor's offices all week long. Larry came back from being on a cruise with his wife. I was glad to see him. I told him I went to see Ken and he said, "Good." But he looked so empty and sad. I asked, "What's wrong?"

Now he and I were pretty open with each other most of the time, so we were comfortable telling each other personal things. "Well," he said, "my wife told me she hates me while we were on our cruise."

How is it, I wondered, *that I can see his pain so clearly and feel it like my own?* I told him, "Larry, you have got to start unlocking your own life's mess." I swore we were sent to each other, to help one another, or just to know we were not alone.

The rest of the week flew by, and Mat went for his meeting with Ken. He came home and said that they talked, and we both had an appointment in one week. It seemed so easy, but again, I smelled a rat!

I couldn't wait a whole week to talk to Ken, so I called him and met with him a few days later. "Well, what do you think, Ken?"

"I saw a few things, but I'm really looking hard because of what you have told me, but I will tell you this, whatever is in this man is buried deep and I don't know if you'll ever get to the core of it."

I couldn't even stand going home anymore, but I had nowhere else to go. Grace was still there, and I won't leave her. I called my mom crying. "Mom, the devil is dancing on my back, and I don't know what to do."

She tried to comfort me. "You'll be OK, honey."

I knew she didn't know what to say, but it's nice to know she's there.

My body hurt so much from therapy, and my heart hurt from the agony in my marriage. I just wanted the truth so I could move forward. Mat still claimed none of this was true.

Tonight, we both met with Ken together for the first time. I drove alone in Grace's car. I didn't know what's going to happen, and I wanted to make sure I had transportation of my own.

We went into Ken's office and sat down. The stress level was so high that I felt like throwing up.

Ken started. "Well, Ann, why don't you go first?"

"OK," I said. I just wanted to put it out there and blast it open so I did. "I think my husband is gay and has known this since high school. I believe this has a lot to do with the anger he always has in him!" I turned to my husband, and his face turned white. His eyes lit with fire.

Ken turned the conversation back to Mat. "How would you like to respond?"

Mat was looking at me as if I was the devil himself. He heated up very quickly and became very angry and started making up crazy lies about me.

An hour flew by. Ken finally said, "We have to stop for now because I have to go to a meeting."

I looked at Ken, and I pleaded with him, "You can't leave us like this." For the first time in my life, I was afraid of my husband.

Mat left the office in a rage of anger.

"I'm so sorry, Ann," Ken said, "that I have to leave you like this, but I have to go to this meeting."

"It's OK, Ken, I understand. I am nervous about going home though. I'll see you in a week."

I left Ken's office and went to the parking lot. Mat was pulling out and I actually thought he was going to hit me with the car. I was so glad I had Grace's car even though it was a junker because I didn't have to be in the same car with him. I drove Grace to school in the morning in this old bomb of a car that she and Michael both used for school, and she took the bus home.

The next day I tried to call Mat at work. I knew he was there, but he won't pick up the phone. After the fifth phone call within an hour, I left this message: "If you don't communicate with me, then we have nothing!"

He called back within one minute. He's angry from the night before. He shouted, "I want a divorce, and you're not allowed to talk to me unless it's about our kids. I would leave tonight, but I have nowhere to go!"

It was all very stressful but for some odd reason, I stayed very calm, just as if God had His hand on my shoulder. I said, "You have been working all week. You come here, and I'll leave for the weekend." Mat came home and went to bed. The next day was Saturday morning, and I woke up early. I left at 6:30 a.m.

I only had two dollars to my name, and I was still in therapy. *Where am I going to go?* I drove around for a while and then I met with Larry for therapy. He was very kind to me. "Where are you going to go? Did you eat?" We talked that morning for about three hours. He always made me feel better. He had his own problems with his wife, and somehow we understood each other's pain like no one else could.

I managed to stay out of the house till 9:00 p.m. I was tired, so I just went to sleep. The next morning I got up and went to get a cup of coffee. To my surprise, Mat was waiting for me. "Can we talk?" he asked.

"I thought I wasn't supposed to talk to you."

"OK, I had to be a smart-ass just for a moment. Let me get a cup of coffee."

We both sat down.

"What are we going to do?" he said to me. It was like a little boy asking his mom what to do.

I softly replied, "All I know is we have to be smart because we don't have a lot."

He started sobbing uncontrollably. I was very calm, almost cold at that moment.

He started saying, "I can't live like this anymore!" Out of the corner of my eye, I could see he was grabbing his chest.

At this, I spun around quickly. "What do you mean you can't live like what?"

He caught himself and said, "You know, fighting like this."

"But I haven't even raised my voice and we're not fighting, we're just talking."

He became more hysterical, sobbing out of control. I stood up and tried to take his hand. He pulled it away. His behavior was so odd to me.

I said, "Have you been molested?"

"No! No!" he said.

I sat down again. "This isn't about us, this is about you. You need help."

This was the deep Ken has been trying to get to, but he was right, it was so deep. Too deep for me to help Mat. I calmed down and told him I would find a counselor to help him, and I would get him in as soon as possible.

I saw Larry the next day. He walked in, and I started to cry. He just held me and said, "You'll be all right." He gave me the name of a counselor that his wife had seen at one time and who deals with this kind of stuff.

The counselor was an older woman, which I think will be better for a man. Mat never had dealt with men well. He was much better with women and especially an older woman.

Her name is Janice Chonski. I called her and set up an appointment after talking with her for about an hour. She was partly retired, but when I told her all that was going on, she found it very odd and was very interested in the case. I told her we had very little money and cannot afford her, but she was so interested in the case that she charged very little. There was only enough for one of us to seek help and he needed it way more than I do.

My mom called every day to give me support, not saying much but just listening to me. One day she asked me to go to the church and talked to the priest. Even though I was a very strong Catholic, I don't go to the priest for advice, but I do go to ask about an annulment through the church. Of course, I had to tell him why, and even though, I had no real answer yet, no proof, everything was pointing in one direction.

I had not known this priest that long, for I just moved to this community not too long ago, even so he still gave me his opinion. "That man is not gay! He probably just has low testosterone like I do."

"Really! I'll tell you what, Father, when I find out the truth, if I'm wrong, I will take you to dinner anywhere you want to go, but if I'm right you will take me."

"OK, deal," he said.

I tried to concentrate on therapy and just getting better. My lawyer was having me go see doctors and get proof. He wanted me to set the case up and get his paycheck going.

The week finally was through, and Mat met with Janice. When he came home, he's real happy.

"Well, how did it go?" I asked.

"Well, we've decided I'm heterosexual."

"OK, OK, what else?"

"Well, you know I masturbate."

I replied, "All men masturbate, but they also have sex with their wives. To just masturbate and ignore me is twisted!"

By this point, I was crying and could barely get the words out, but I continued. "Please pick up a sword and ram it through my chest because that would hurt less than this does."

I had to walk away. I was crying so hard I couldn't breathe well.

Mat stopped me. "The therapist wants to see you now."

My crying turned to anger. "Oh bring her on. I'm so ready to get a woman's point of view on this."

He grew angry right back and snapped back with, "I'm sure you two will love to rip me apart!"

Now Grace was in the house, and I didn't want to involve her, so I went to my bedroom, shut the door, and sat in the dark by myself. "God, please help me. I can't condemn this man if I don't have the truth. Please show me the truth so I know what I'm dealing with. I can't move in any direction because I don't know the truth." I was so tired mentally and physically that I fell asleep on my bed.

It was Easter, and we went to my mother's house to celebrate. Michael was home from college just for the day. Things were really strained, and everyone knew it. We had two cars because Mat was taking Michael back early to school, and Grace and I were staying longer. She had the week off school and was going to work this week with her dad to help him with filing. He was keeping her very close to him.

Two days after Easter Sunday it's midday and the phone rang. It's Mat calling from work and Grace was with him.

"Hey, I just took a month-long job in California. Can you drive me to the airport a week from now?"

"You're going to leave in the middle of this?" I couldn't believe my ears. What was he doing? What was he running from? Again the smell of a rat! He never traveled for work before. "Fine! I'll drive you to the airport."

Later that evening after they came home, Grace came to me. She was upset. I had tried so hard to keep her out of all of this, but it was impossible now. After all, she lived at home with us and didn't have the luxury of escaping to a college dorm like Michael does!

"Mom," she started, "I told Dad to call you and talk to you before he did this, but he wouldn't. Mom, he became really happy after they told him he could go."

"What do you mean, they told him he could go? Didn't they ask him to go?"

"No, Mom, he found the position online and applied for it through the company."

A low growl started deep in me that day but still nothing was concrete.

The weekend came, and it was the Feast of Divine Mercy, a big feast day to my family. We were new to this church, and it was very different from what we were used to. On this day, you must go to confession. Grace and I showed up and then Mat showed up on his own. There's only the three of us there. It's so awkward.

I went first. I sat face-to-face with the priest and went through confession. When we're done, he stopped me and said, "How are things going?"

"Not good at all," I said. "He's leaving for California in two days for a month."

"What! Oh, that's not good at all."

I was frustrated, and I thought, *Really? Ya think?! You're darn right it's not good. Let the chips fall where they may.*

I left and went home with Grace. She went to her room and just shut the door.

I was in the kitchen cleaning up, and Mat walked in. I continued what I was doing. Finally, he kissed me on the cheek. The kind of kiss you would give to your mother. He asked me, "Can I hug you?"

"Absolutely not!" I replied.

He started to plead with me. "Come on, honey. I just got lazy, that's all."

By this point I have had enough with the games. Lazy! Lazy! Seventeen years with no touch at all between us. I mean, I could believe that if I were four hundred pounds and flies were buzzing around me, but that's not the case. "You're not going to cloud my head by touching me now. You go to California. I need time to search my soul. I have asked you over and over throughout our marriage what's wrong and you never answer me."

I turned to walk away and heard him say under his breath, "I tried to tell you!"

I spun around so fast. "You never tried! It's two words, I'm gay!"

He pushed me out of the way with his arm aggressively and said, "I'm no gay blade."

I shout one more time, "You are gay! No man can lie next to a woman that long and not touch her unless he's gay."

It's Sunday again the next day, and I was in my own car with Grace and he was in his. I went to the priest after mass. "What did you say to him yesterday?" I asked.

He was angry and said, "It took a lot for that man to come forward and approach you. He is trying."

I snapped back, "I thought confessions are private, and he's trying all right, he's trying to cover his tracks. I'll have my answers soon enough and then I will make you eat your words!"

The next day as I was driving Mat to the airport, I tried to talk peacefully to him. I felt so low and he seemed very unstable to me. I asked him how he felt.

"I feel like I'm leaving with a hole in my heart," he said. He started to cry. I just felt numb. No emotions at all.

I drove home by myself after I dropped him off, and my brain was going a mile a minute. There was this great feeling of tension lifted off me, but I felt so alone.

I called my mom to talk. She always built me up with her love and comforted me as much as she could. "Ann," she said. "Let him go. You'll be fine, honey. You take care of Grace and Michael. You can always come live with me."

The next day Grace brought the mail in. As she thumbed through it, she came across a bank statement and handed it to me. It was addressed to only Mat. I found that odd since we always had joint everything. I opened it to find out that he had opened an account by himself. Grace asked me to explain what this was. "Well, honey," I said, "I think he is stealing money from us."

"What do you mean, Mom? We don't have money."

"I know, and he's trying to hide it for himself."

Grace was furious. "You wait till I see him!"

"Oh no, honey, you leave this to me because this will reveal itself when the time is right!"

I called Mat the next day. I started by saying, "Hey, I think something is wrong with your check deposit into our account. The normal amount that goes in weekly is less $100."

He replied, very casually, "Really? I'll have to check into it."

He had no idea that I saw the new account statement. He lied so easily to me, and it was the first concrete piece of the puzzle. "You do that," I said.

Now I was to meet with Janice the next day. She called to tell me that her husband had a mild heart attack, and she would have to postpone our meeting until the following week. My head was about to explode. "Janice," I said, "did you know that he left for a month to California?"

"What? Oh, he's running away," she said.

"I know that, Janice. I can't wait to sit and talk to you."

All through the week I went to therapy and Larry was there. He just sat and held my hand and talked to me. Every time we talked I could see the pain of rejection in his eyes too. I told him all the time now that God had sent us to each other. Brought together out of pain. It really was a strong connection.

The morning finally came to meet with Janice. I tried not to tell Grace any of this because things were hard enough at school for her right now. She really needed a friend her own age to talk to.

Janice's office was out of her home. I entered and just waited. She came in and said hello finally. She looked like a mom, maybe in her sixties, grayish-blond hair worn in an older style. She's a little on the chunky side, an ordinary-looking person; not at all like a therapist. "Please take a seat next to me," she said.

I sat down and started to talk, but didn't even knew where to begin, so I just dive in straight on. I told her all about the thoughts of him being gay and about this underlying anger that's always present. She surprised me by saying, "I don't see gay at all, but I do see, maybe, abandonment."

"I'm sorry, I'm not crazy," I told her. "I think you're wrong, but time will tell."

Janice and I talked for a short time. She knew Larry and his wife. She also knew of their problems. She asked me if Larry had helped me. "Janice," I said, "if it wasn't for Larry, I think I would have lost my mind by now! Janice, I swear God sent us to each other."

When I left there, I felt like I was up against a very good con artist because Mat had this woman's pity in his hand. I felt like I had underestimated him.

As the week moved on, I was still talking to Mat daily while he was in California. He told me my oldest sister, Jean, who lives in California, had called him and asked him to lunch or to meet with him just to talk. I didn't need anyone in the middle of this, and I was mad that she had gone behind my back to him. I asked him about his paycheck again. He told bald-face lies right to me about it. "I still haven't had time to check into it yet," he said. Lie no. 2!

The next day I was back in therapy for my back, and I was waiting for Larry. I called Jean in California and asked her what she thought she's doing. She tried to explain it away with some stupid made-up story about her daughter wanting to see Mat, but I was furious. Her daughter is fifteen and was never close to Mat. "Jean, you stay out of this. Do you hear me? Or there will be bad blood between us forever. Now you call him and cancel this lunch right now. Back off!"

Larry walked in and I hang the phone up. "What's wrong?" he asked.

"Nothing, let's get started," I snapped.

I called my mom and told her about Jean and what she's doing. My mom asked me, "Why does she need to see him?"

"My thoughts exactly. I am confused enough, and she doesn't need to get in the way."

My mom tried to comfort me but with little success. Even though Mom is very old-fashioned and doesn't really understand what gay is, she saw Mat tearing me and my kids up. It killed her because she couldn't do anything about it.

The week moved on. I called Mat to talk about some household issues because, after all, we're married. The conversation quickly turned. I was pleading with him for answers. I said to him, "I don't understand. You say you love me, but you won't fight for me. Any man who loves a woman would—" I stopped in the middle of the sentence. "Oh my god! You don't want to fight for me. You want me to divorce you!"

Then dead silence. I was sobbing this time, and I told him I had to go.

The next morning I called him back. I very calmly said, "I'm getting a lawyer. When you return home, you need to move out of the bedroom, and you need to go back to Janice."

He agreed. He insisted that he be there when we tell the kids, but what he didn't know was that "we" were done and now it's just "me."

I went by my own rules now. He had finally driven the sword completely through my heart.

CHAPTER 9

Keeping My Kids Together

IT'S STILL ANOTHER TWO WEEKS before Mat came back and there was a lot to do. Where do I begin? My children. I called Michael and told him I was coming to meet with him for lunch today. "OK, Mom, I'll be there."

It's an hour-and-a-half ride, so I had some time to think and cry and pray.

I arrived at the cafeteria at Michael's college. He's already there. "Hi, honey," I said as I give him a hug.

"Hi, Mom, what's up?"

"How do I even start this conversation with you? Honey, your father and I have had some issues in our marriage that are not right. You're old enough to know that men and women touch and have sex. Well, your father won't touch me and hasn't for a very long time. I know you don't want to hear about our sex life, but you need to know that I think he is gay. I am getting a lawyer and starting a divorce."

"Wow, Mom, I don't know what to say." The look on Michael's face at the moment will be burned into my memory forever.

"You don't have to say anything, honey. I just want you to know what's going on."

We finished our lunch, and when I left, he seemed to be so off, his mind probably trying to sort it all out.

Mat called this morning to tell me my sister Jean had met him for lunch. I asked him why, what did she want? He said he didn't know. Now I was angry at her for not staying out of this, and I didn't trust either one of them anymore. The new question on my mind was just who could I trust.

I was waiting for Grace to come home from school. It's time to sit down and tell her what's going on. She came in and I told her to sit down. I tried to explain to her just like I did with Michael. Grace had always noticed the littlest of details. "Mom, I've always known my dad was different," she told me. "All the other dads would be gathered around a sports event, acting like guys, and my dad would be in the corner with his legs crossed and a cup of coffee in his hand. I guess I was just a little girl, and I didn't know what to call it at the time."

I was stunned. Grace was far beyond her years. An old soul. "How is it you can see so clearly, and I cannot see at all!"

"Don't worry, Mom. We'll make it."

"Grace, I'm getting a lawyer, and I'm divorcing your father. I can't trust anything he says to me anymore."

Mat called the next day. I think he was trying to tell me the truth, but he just couldn't say the words. He's crying on the phone. "I have ruined your life," he said. "I have ruined a life!"

Now I knew he's just not stable at this point, so I was very easy on him. "Mat, I would not say ruined, but what you have done to me and your children is wrong! You need help from someone who can deal with this level of problems. This is way above my head. You need to go back to Janice when you come home."

I called my mom for support. "I feel so broken, Mom," I told her.

"You'll be OK, honey. I love you."

"Thanks, Mom, I needed that."

The next day I went to see Father Bob. I told him what had been going on. I wanted to start an annulment. "This was a lie right on the altar of God," I told him. "From the very beginning, from day one! I have no money, no job, no car of my own, and I'm still very injured."

It's time to start telling people that I'm divorcing. I called my good friend Wendy Davenport. We've been friends for years though she lives far away, and we only talk every six months or so. "Ann, you need a lawyer. My husband's cousin is a divorce lawyer. Give her a call and get some advice."

"Thanks, Wendy."

I was back in therapy with Larry later that week. I told him that I was divorcing my husband and I was calling a lawyer later that day.

He said, "Ann, how are you going to pay for it?"

"I have a small IRA account with about $3,000 in it. I guess I will have to use it."

"How are you going to pay the bills and get a car?"

"I don't know, Larry. I will go to God. He always takes care of me!"

He gave me a hug, and it felt so good to me. He kissed me, and I knew it felt good to both of us. A kiss driven by our sheer pain connection. Whatever our relationship is, who cares at this point? Not me or him. It was comforting through such pain. And we both had so much of it.

I went home, and my body was feeling better so it's time to call the lawyer. Her name is Linda Adams. She had been divorced and remarried, so she understood the pain of it all. "Ann, you need a divorce. Don't feel bad. You need to move forward."

"I know and I'm ready. How much do I need for this?"

"It starts at $2,500 and up."

"All right, I will get the money. Thank you and I will be in touch."

I cashed out the only money I had left in the world. I called my mom. "Ann," she said, "you need to move back with me."

"Thank you anyway, Mom, but everything I have is here. I don't know how I'm going to make it, but I'll die trying."

Mat was returning home today. I had to pick him up from the airport. Grace was a little upset, and I knew things were going to be tense. "Mom, do you want me to go with you?" she asked.

"No, honey, you just go to school and don't worry."

I picked Mat up early in the afternoon. Things were tense and the drive home was quiet.

"Mat, you need to start seeing Janice again," I finally said. "She can help you."

"OK, I will. There for a few weeks I really thought of killing myself."

"Mat! You know that is never the answer," I said. "You're not an evil man. You need to look in the mirror and like yourself. You have become all screwed up in your mind somewhere along the way, and you need to fix it."

The rest of the ride home was quiet. Mat just stared straight ahead as if he was in another world.

When we got home, Mat moved into the spare bedroom. I felt some relief that he was out of the bedroom now. Things were just weird now. All screwed up.

Grace came home from school and said hello and kept on walking right to her bedroom. I could feel how upset she was, having such a hard time in school and with our home and family about to explode. How do I keep everyone together and not fall apart myself?

CHAPTER 10

The Divorce

I WAS MY FIRST NIGHT in my bedroom alone now. I closed the door and sat on the floor next to the bed in the dark. I looked out the doorwall at the stars of the night. Tears slowly started to run down my cheeks as I thought about how bad things were. I gave everything in this marriage just to find out I have been betrayed from day one. The fog was starting to clear, and I saw that I was standing in a pool of filth. I wanted to crawl out and scrape the scum off my body. How must my children feel?

I wake up the next day; as the morning started, Mat came out of his room. He told me, "I think we need to talk."

I said, "I would suggest we use the same lawyer to save money. After all, we really don't have much to fight over. We can work this out ourselves. I will set up an appointment for us to meet with the lawyer."

"OK, Ann."

"I will tell you right now, Mat, you will have to sign over the house to me."

He became angry. "What for, I worked hard for this house too!"

"Well, Mat, I have to finish raising our children by myself, and they need a home."

"Ann, they're my children too."

"Mat, your tour of duty is over. I will go into court wearing a GAY sign across my chest if I have to, but you will sign it over to me, and I will have to finish paying for it somehow. Haven't you done enough to us! If you want a fight, I'm ready, but believe me, my father taught me well."

"Ann, I don't want to fight with you."

"Good choice, Mat! It's the first smart thing I've heard you say lately."

He finally left for work and I felt some relief.

I called my mom. She listened so patiently to me. She always put wind under my wings when I feel there is none to be found. "I love you, Mom! Thanks for being there for me."

"I love you too, honey. You're going to be all right."

I wanted to feel better any way I could today, so a shower and makeup always helped. As I was dressing, the phone rang. It's Kyle, the lawyer from my car accident. "Ann, I need to meet with you soon to get more information about the accident."

"OK, Kyle, but I have to tell you that I'm getting a divorce, and things are getting crazy here."

"What! Why are you getting a divorce, Ann?"

"Well, Kyle, after twenty-eight years of marriage to my husband, I have found out that he is gay." I started to cry.

"Wow, I am sorry, Ann. I'm divorced too, and it's hard."

"My whole life has been a lie, Kyle. I feel so stupid. How could I miss something like this? I have been betrayed since the day I met Mat."

"OK, OK, OK, Ann, try to calm down. Let's meet next week, and we'll talk."

"That's fine, Kyle. I'll see you then."

A week passed, and I was losing so much weight. My clothes were just hanging off my body right now. It's like an instant diet.

I was going to therapy every day, and Larry and I talked a lot. He kept me sane most of the time. Easter had just passed and Grace, Michael, and I went alone to my mother's house. How strange it felt already.

Now Mat and I were meeting with Linda Adams to get the divorce papers started. Even though she was my lawyer, he had decided to use her too.

We hammered out all the details as fast as we could without too much arguing, but it was tense. "Mat and Ann, you will have to fill out the paperwork together at home so it is correct for the court. Also, the court requires that because you have a child under eighteen years of age, you must attend a parenting class together."

I felt like throwing up my lunch at that point. I wanted to tell everyone the reason why my marriage was destroyed. Then there would be no question as to my parenting or anything for that matter, but we had to go, so I just shut up.

Grace came home from school later. She hated it there. I hated to make her life any more awful than it was.

"How was your day, Mom?"

"Well, I have a lot on my mind, honey."

"How are we going to make it, Mom? Can we pay our bills?"

"Grace, I don't know what tomorrow holds for us, but God will show us the way. I'm going to have to take pain meds and go back to work somewhere."

"Mom, I can help. I can get a job and pay a bill or two!"

"Honey, you are a sixteen-year-old girl. All I need is for you to go to school and be a teenage for now. Let me worry about the bills. I love you, Grace. We'll be OK, don't worry."

Another week passed and Mat returned to therapy with Janice. Even though the tension in the house was bad, I still tried to be kind. "How is therapy going, Mat?"

"Fine!"

"Is she helping you sort things out?"

"Yes, OK."

"Mat, you need to find a place to live."

"I know, Ann."

"Have you looked for an apartment, Mat?"

"I don't want an apartment. I want a house."

"Mat, you are not even thinking clear. You don't know where your life is going to go, and you don't have any money."

"I can borrow out of my 401(k) up to half for a down payment on a house."

"I think you're foolish, Mat, but your life is no longer my concern."

"Ann, you are much better at finding a house than I am. Would you please help me find one?"

Everything in me wants to say *no*, but I think God would want me to be kind. "Fine, Mat, I will start looking."

The tension in the house was so great. It's evening, and I was locked in my bedroom because I didn't want to see Mat.

There's a knock on the bedroom door. It's Grace. "Mom, can I just come in?"

"Sure, honey. What's up?"

"I just don't want to be out there with Dad. I just want to stay in here with you."

"It's OK, Grace. you can come in here anytime, and you can just sleep in here with me. Bring your homework, and I'll help you."

"Thanks, Mom! When I was a kid, Mom, I always looked at you and Dad as one, but now that you're apart, I see you as you and him as him, and I don't like him. I now realize that it's always been you that I have seen. It's like he's hidden behind you to cover up."

My heart wrenched and tears welled up in my eyes. I could feel Grace's confusion and pain about her dad. She adored him so and now the star had fallen from eyes. "Come on, honey, let's get some sleep. Tomorrow is a new day."

Morning came and I had physical therapy with Allen today. He did not know what was going on with my personal life, but he kept questioning me. I finally broke down and told him about the divorce.

He said, "I'm sorry, Ann." He tried to console me, but I really missed Larry.

I had to meet with Kyle by noon. He wanted to go over the car accident with me.

"Hi, Ann, come into my office and have a seat. How are you doing?"

"I'm holding up."

"Ann, can't you just make a deal with Mat?"

"Like what kind of a deal, Kyle?"

"Well, that you stay married, but you both do your own thing and see who you want to."

"Kyle, you are crazy! So I should make a deal with the devil? Is that what you're saying?"

"Well, not quite like that, but at least you won't be in such a poor spot."

"Kyle, I would rather live in a refrigerator box than live a lie! Are we done here because you have made me sick to my stomach now."

"Ann, I'm just trying to help you."

"Kyle, I can do anything with my hand in God's hand, but I will not live a lie."

I got back into the car I had been driving—my kids' beat-up bomb of a car. I drove Grace in the mornings, and she took the bus home.

I put my head back for a moment. My body was so sore I needed some drugs for pain.

I called Michael at school to see how he was doing. "Hi, honey, how are you?"

"I'm fine, Mom."

I was fighting back the tears, and my voice was cracking. "Michael, do you want to talk to me about your dad?"

"No, Mom, not really."

"But, honey, you have to talk about it sometime. Or it will fester into a volcano before you know it."

"Mom, I don't want to talk to you about it. My college offers free counseling for students. Maybe I'll go talk to someone there."

"OK, Michael. I love you, honey."

"I know you do, Mom, and I love you too."

It had been a long hard day, and I wanted to go and sit with God in the church for a while before Grace and Mat got home. I found such peace in front of the tabernacle that even if I just sit in silence I know that the Lord's arms are around me. It gave me strength to carry on.

Grace came home from school. "I hate it here, Mom."

"Grace, I'm sorry. What can I do to help you?"

"Nothing. I just hate my life."

"I know things are bad right now, but we will get through this."

Mat walked in and the tension started. We barely talked, and finally Grace and I locked ourselves in the bedroom for the night.

The week had flown by again. My divorce lawyer Linda called. "Ann, the paperwork is ready, but Mat has to be legally served with the papers. It will cost you about $300 to have someone serve them."

"Linda, I don't have that kind of money. What if I find someone to serve them?"

"You can do that, Ann, as long as it's not you."

"OK, fine, just send them to me, and I will take care of it."

I called Mat at work, and I explained to him about the cost to have him served with papers. "Mat, I have called my friend Dana Cole, and she has agreed to serve the papers to you to save the money. Mat, I just want you to be prepared."

"Fine, Ann, do what you have to do!"

Dana had been my lifelong friend. "Dana is just trying to help us, Mat!"

"Whatever, Ann!" He hung the phone up on me.

I kept telling Mat he needed to move out, but I knew until he got a house he will stay as long as he can. So I started to look for a house for him. I was out all week with a real estate person looking between therapy and trying to run the house!

I came home from grocery shopping. It's hot, and I'm hurting all over. Grace was home from school, and Mat was home from work. Mat won't even help carry the groceries in, so Grace said, "Mom, I'll help you."

"Thank you, honey."

Then I said to Mat, "Please just open the door and let the dog in."

Mat was in a really foul mood. "Do it yourself, Ann!"

"Mat, I have my hands full, just open the door!"

Grace stepped up. "I'll get it, Mom. Dad, Mom does everything for you, and you are just being an asshole!"

Mat stomped off to the bedroom and slammed the door.

"Grace, it's OK, honey. I'll take care of your dad, and you don't have to fight my battles for me."

"I know, Mom, he's such an asshole now."

"Come on. Get your homework. We'll get some snacks, and we'll lock ourselves in the bedroom tonight."

"OK, Mom, sounds good."

A few days later, the divorce papers arrived by certified mail. I called Dana. "They're here, Dana. Can we get this over today?"

"Sure, Ann. I'll be there this afternoon."

"OK, thanks."

I called Mat at work to warn him that this was going to happen today. I just wanted this over, and I didn't want Grace to be here for this.

Mat came home, and Grace was at school still. Dana and I had been waiting. Dana stood up when Mat walked in. "Here, Mat, I'm sorry. I know this is a hard day."

He pulled the papers out of her hand and walked to the bedroom, his place of refuge now.

Dana said, "Ann, I'm going to go so you and Mat can talk."

"Thanks for your help, Dana. I'll call you later."

I went to Mat's room. "You could have at least thanked her for her help, Mat," I said. "She's just trying to save us money we don't have."

He just glared at me with hatred in his eyes.

I was determined to find Mat a house because he needed to go. He was causing the whole house to be crazy.

The following Tuesday I set up three house showings for Mat to see. One of the houses needed a lot of work but had great possibilities. He liked it and put in a bid on it. I knew it would take time to close, but still it was in the works. Yahoo!

My sister Beth called me because she had found out about the divorce. "What is going on, Ann?"

"I have found out he's gay!"

"You're lying, Ann. He is not gay."

"Beth, why would I destroy my marriage of twenty-eight years over nothing? My whole family, life, household are falling apart, and you call me a liar."

"Well, I don't believe it, Ann."

"Beth, you believe whatever you want, but this is not your life."

Once again it's like a baseball bat to the back of my knees. Beth always wanted to control things, and this time she had become very mean.

I was supposed to have therapy with Larry. I was crying so hard this morning. I just couldn't pull myself together. I called Larry's office. He answered the phone because it's still early. "Larry, this is Ann. I can't come in today."

"Why, Ann?"

"I can't stop crying, and I feel so low."

"Ann, it's not good for you to sit home. You just get yourself here, and I will put you in a room right away."

"OK, Larry. I'll be there soon."

I arrived at Larry's office and he was waiting for me. He took me to a room right away. He closed the door and held me in his arms. He could see how much pain I was in physically and mentally. I was shaking. "Ann, calm down," he said.

"I'm trying, Larry."

He looked into my eyes and kissed me tenderly on the lips. It felt so good to kiss him. I knew pain was bringing us together, but he made me feel wanted and like a beautiful woman, something I haven't felt in a long, long time.

Nevertheless, I pulled away. Larry was married still! I didn't want to be the whore here.

"Please don't touch me. You know how vulnerable I am right now. It feels nice to both of us because we're both starved for love."

"I know, Ann."

"Who sent you, Larry, God or the devil?"

"God, I hope."

The rest of the day my heart felt a little better. It was like Larry was breathing life into me again. No one liked to be around when trouble happens, but Larry never turned away from me.

It's afternoon, and I have started to exercise a lot now. It helped me strengthen my back and relieve some stress. When I got home, Mat was there. He told me they had accepted his bid on the house, and they were going to start the paperwork.

"Great, Mat." I went to my bedroom where Grace was already waiting for me. "Come on, Mom, I've got some snacks for us."

"OK, honey. How was school today?"

"I hate school, and I hate swimming more."

"What's wrong, Grace?"

"My swim coach is really mean to us. He just yells at me all the time in front of everyone. He even throws orange pills at us when we're swimming to get our attention."

"What? Have you said anything to him?"

"No."

"Why not?"

"Because he's the coach."

"OK, Grace, but you don't have to take that from anyone. I will be at your practice tomorrow."

"Thanks, Mom."

The next day I showed up for Grace's practice. I saw her across the pool, and I just watched the coach. He was not very nice to the girls. He called them maggots and told them to get into the pool. I got Grace's attention, and I called her over. "Grace, if he yells at you, I want you to stand up for yourself. Walk off the pool deck and I will be right here."

"I love you, Mom."

"You stand strong, Grace."

The coach backed off because he knew I was there sitting in the stands, and there was no need for a showdown. He left her alone and just didn't talk to her anymore. Grace learned from it. I wanted to give her strength.

I had to call Father Bob to talk about an annulment in the church for what I thought was a marriage. I feel like my whole life had been a lie.

"Hi, Father Bob, this is Ann DeChallis."

"Oh, hi, Ann."

"Well, it's time to talk annulment and how to go about it. Where do I start?"

"You're sure he's gay?"

"Yes, I am."

"Wow! My gaydar must be off. Well, Ann, I think you should go back to your old church and talk to your pastor there. It is $200 to do it from here, and it's free there. I will help you fill out the paperwork, but run it through the old parish!"

"OK, I will call and see what I have to do. I will call you back when I need you to help."

I hung up the phone and called my old parish right away. I finally got to speak to Father Jim Richards, our old priest. "Hi, Father Jim, this is Ann DeChallis. Do you remember me?"

"Yes, Ann, what can I help you with?"

I explained the whole story about Mat to him. Now in my mind I knew for some reason this was not the first time he had heard something like this. He said to me, "And you never knew any of this before you were married?"

"Absolutely not, Father Jim! I would never have had any part of this not then and not now."

He became angry at the whole situation. Then he started to help me. "Ann, I will send you the paperwork, and we can run it through your mother's address so you don't have to pay any fees."

"Thank you for your help, Father Jim."

I called my mother to tell her what I was doing and how I had to run the annulment.

"Hi, Mom."

"Hi, honey. How are you today?"

"I'm OK. I talked to the priest at our old church about an annulment, and he said that if I said I lived with you they would do it for free."

"Will the church give you an annulment?"

"Well, Mom, I don't know. But Mat has destroyed our family and he has betrayed me from the minute I met him. Our marriage, if you can call it that, was a joke. I will not let him destroy my religion. This is what the church says I should do so I am going for it."

"You're right, Ann. You hold your head up, honey. You have done nothing wrong."

"I love you, Mom. Now you will get some letters from the archdiocese as it goes along. When they come, please just put them aside, and I will pick them up when I see you next. They are clearly marked."

"OK, honey. You stand strong now, Ann."

"OK, Mom. I'll talk to you later."

A week later, Father Jim sent the papers to start the annulment. The packet was huge, and I was overwhelmed. As I read what was needed to start, emotions came over me. I had to stop for a while.

A few hours later, I tried again. Five people that have known us for a while have to write their versions of what they saw! I felt so embarrassed by all of this. Now I had to ask people to write this on my behalf! Who will I ask?

I called Father Bob and told him that the paperwork was here and how there was too much. He told me to just do a page a day. Good advice.

It's time for Mat and I to sit down and fill out the divorce papers together. This is so hard to do. "Well, Mat," I say, "let's just take one section at a time."

"OK, fine."

"All the personal information we can fill out first."

Next we had to list our assets. "Well, we don't have much," I said. "Our house and our car."

"OK, Ann."

"Next is our bank accounts. Well, that's easy. We only have one bank account."

"Sure, Ann, and this second one here." Now I knew that Mat had been stealing money for himself and setting it aside, but he didn't know that I knew.

"Mat, we don't have a second account."

"Yes, Ann. It's this old account that we had years ago."

"Mat, I closed that account a long time ago." Now it's like trapping a rat in a corner, so I was watching him closely. How will he lie to me? What will his face look like? We shall see!

"It never closed, Ann."

"Really, Mat. Well, if it is truly our account, pull it up on the computer and show me my name on it."

"Well, OK, Ann."

As we both stare at the computer I'm watching him sweat.

"Wow, that's weird, it is only my name."

Now the rat was caught.

"Mat, you son of a bitch. You opened this account to steal money for you. Taking food off our table just because you are a coward."

"Ann," he dodged, "I have to go pick up Grace."

"Go ahead and run, Mat, but remember this: God sees everything."

Now Mat couldn't leave the house fast enough. I was so angry at this point; I needed to calm down. I went outside to work in my garden. It's like therapy to me. Mat returned about half an hour later without Grace. He came outside to talk to me.

"Ann, I didn't lie to you about the bank account."

I stopped what I was doing and looked at him. "I gave you everything, Mat. I gave you my hand in marriage. I gave you my life, my heart, and my soul. And you have betrayed me! You are a no-good, lying, cheating, con artist, and I am done with you. You are a rat caught in his own trap! Now get out of my face. You make me sick to my stomach."

He stared at me and I ignored him. He walked away as cold as could be. Not a sign of emotion at all.

Mat went to pick up Grace an hour later and brought her home. She knew that something had happened. I tried to keep her out of this, but she's always questioning me, and I won't lie to her. I won't sugarcoat anything. There had been enough lying in this house already.

Mat got in his car and left for a while.

Grace came to me right away. "Mom, what happened?"

"Well, Grace, I told you there was a time and a place for everything. I caught your father in a bald-faced lie about the money he had been stealing from us."

"What did he say, Mom?"

"He just kept lying to me, Grace, until I called him out on it. He could not con me anymore!"

"Mom, I wish he would just leave here and leave us alone."

"Soon, honey. And this too shall pass."

Mat left for work earlier and earlier now. The tension had mounted so high in the house now, it's almost unbearable.

The annulment papers kept staring me down. It's a long process to go through, years sometimes. But I was determined in spite of everything else on my plate. You couldn't even start the annulment until you were legally divorced, but there was a lot to prepare. I had to ask five people to fill out their own paperwork on my behalf first. The one person I think of right away was my mom. She stood by me always. Next I called my sister Kathy who said she would do it with my mom so they could help each other.

Now I needed three more people, so I reached out to my friends—Dana, Wendy, and Peggy. Dana Cole and Peggy Dublin were friends of mine since childhood, so they had been around. Wendy Davenport and I met early on in our young adult life and became friends quickly. Peggy and Dana were glad to help, and Wendy was so ready to get going on the paperwork. She asked me to mail it right away to her. "Ann, when I'm done with the paperwork, there will be no question in their minds that he is gay, and he did this to you," she told me.

Now I looked at my part of it. The questions were very hard and personal. Once I started writing though, I couldn't seem to stop. It's like pouring my whole life out onto paper. Details of our relationship and marriage. I cried through some of it, and I got angry through a lot of it, but I got my part done in two days. That should have taken a month!

I took it to Father Bob, and we read it together! He changed the words on a few things, but for the most part, he said it was ready.

"Now what is happening, Father Bob?"

"Well, everyone has to do their part and mail them in and then just wait. There is a committee that reviews these things. It will take a while, and you can't start till you are divorced."

"How long do you think, Father Bob?"

"Anywhere from eight months to three years."

"Wow! OK."

I tucked the papers away safely until I could start the process.

I had therapy the next morning with Larry. I was an emotional mess. He came in the room and hugged me. We started talking and talked for an hour or more. He could see my pain, and he kissed me long and hard. He had his arms wrapped around me tight. It felt so good. I wanted to just go at it, but I pushed him back a little. "Larry, stop. Stop or I'm not going to be able to stop myself, Larry. We are going to get into serious trouble. I don't want to be your whore, Larry."

"OK, Ann, I'll stop."

"I don't want to go home, Larry. I hate it there anyway. But I won't leave Grace alone, and she has school. She's having a hard enough time as it is."

"Where would you go anyway, Ann?"

"I have no money, no friends out here, but even sleeping in the car in a parking lot looks good right now." I would like to go stay with my mom, but Grace had school and the drive was too far. I really didn't trust Mat either. I will just have to tough it for now.

Labor Day weekend was coming, and Grace told Mat she would go with him for the weekend to see his family. Michael was coming home from college for the weekend. I was so looking forward to spending some time alone with my son. I was not going to cry, and we were just going to have a nice weekend together. His friends dropped him off because it was a one-and-a-half-hour drive one way for me, so I was glad they dropped him off.

The next morning an old friend called me. "Hi, Ann, this is Christine Reynolds." Christine and I met through a friend. She liked Mat.

"Good morning, Christine. How are you?"

"Well, I've been better."

"What's wrong?"

"Ann, you are killing Mat!"

"I'm killing Mat?! Give me a break, Christine. Just what do you think Mat is doing to me and my kids?"

"Well, Ann, I had to say something."

"No, you didn't, Christine, but you want your opinion to be heard. Do you feel better now that you have torn me apart when I finally was just trying to stand up?" I started to sob.

"Ann, I have to go."

"Sure you do, Christine." I hung up the phone and I was sobbing out of control.

Michael came into the bedroom. "Mom, are you all right?"

"No, Michael, but I'm trying to be all right. Just remember, son, a lesson in life. When you're down on your knees, people like to kick you in the gut! And you're never ready for who will come out of the woodwork at you."

He stood silent just trying to process it all. As the morning went on, I just couldn't stop crying, and I knew Michael was hurting for me. He just didn't know how to ease the pain.

"Michael, I'm going to take you back to school. Honey, it's just not good for you to watch me cry all weekend. I'm sorry. I so wanted to just spend some alone fun time with you, and now that's ruined."

"OK, Mom, let's go."

As we're driving back to his college dorm, I felt it's a good time to try to get him to talk about it. "But, honey, you have to. Or it will eat you alive."

There was total silence. "Honey, please talk to me."

There still was no answer. "OK. How about if I tell you what I think is going on in your head, and you can tell me if I'm right?"

Still he just stared ahead. "Michael, you see me being hurt and torn apart, right?"

He said nothing, but a tear rolled down his cheek. It broke my heart right in half, but I continued on. "And you want to protect me from all of this, right?"

He nodded his head yes. "I love you, son, but all I need you to do right now is concentrate on your school. Honey, I'm a big girl, and no one can protect me from this except God. Sometimes in life you have to go through things along, and your loved ones can only helplessly watch. I'm so sorry that this is happening to us, but I promise you someday we will see happiness again."

We drove the rest of the way in silence, but I think it was a good talk.

I returned home and stayed alone for the rest of the weekend. That day, I came to the conclusion that if anyone was here to tear me or my family down, they needed to go out of our lives. I was very angry with Christine for destroying my weekend with my son and robbing me of the small joy that had returned for a moment.

Christine called one more time after that, but by then, she had destroyed our friendship. I refused to live in hatred and anger, so I won't, but I would move on to positive things.

Grace and Mat returned home. "How was the weekend, Grace?" I asked.

"It was very strange, Mom. I was so uncomfortable with everyone, mostly Dad. It's all so different."

"I know, honey. We'll get through this together."

Years ago, I had a great friend named Mary McCool. We met when working as cashiers in our first jobs as teens. We attended each other's weddings and were going through having kids at the same time. Then life took over, and we lost touch with each other for the next fifteen years. Mary and I did not see each other or talk to one another, but she was always in the back of my mind. One day, about the time Michael was graduating from high school, my sister Kathy ran into Mary's mother. Kathy knew that Mary was a good friend of mine at one time, and she asked her mom how Mary was doing. Mary's mom told her that Mary was getting a divorce.

Kathy called me and told me this. "Kathy, you must have gotten this wrong. Mary would never divorce."

"Ann, I'm sure of what I heard."

"This bothers me, Kathy. Something is not right. I'm going to try to look her up and call her. Thanks for letting me know."

A few days later, I got ahold of Mary for the first time in fifteen years, and it was as if we never missed a beat. "Mary, what is going on with you? Is this true about a divorce?"

"Yes, Ann, it is. I have found out that my husband is gay!"

My jaw hit the ground. "WHAT!"

"Mary, I am having a graduation party for Michael from high school. Please bring your kids and come. There will be people you know from yesteryear, and your friends."

"I might do that, Ann. I will try."

We hung up, and I was in shock. "Mat, can you believe what has happened to Mary?"

At the time this happened (which was about two years before my own life exploded), I thought Mat was very cold about it. He just shrugged his shoulders and walked away.

Mary never did show up for the party, and I did not want to push her.

Now years later, I was going through the same nightmare. It's crazy how God sends you exactly what you need at that very moment in time. Mary came to mind, and I called her. Her son answered the phone, and she was not home, so I left a message for her to call me back when she could. It's been two years, so I didn't know what's going on in her life, but I knew I needed her. Please, God, let her call me tonight.

The phone rang. "Hi, Ann. This is Mary."

"Thank you for calling back, Mary. I think you and I need to meet for lunch and talk."

"Ann, are you all right?"

"No, Mary. I have found out Mat is gay too."

"Oh my god. How can this happen to both of us?"

"Mary, let's get together and talk."

"OK, Ann."

Mary and I met for lunch. We talked for hours. She validated everything I was feeling and thinking. She knew exactly what I was going through because she already had gone through it.

It was time to start thinking about the future. Mat's house was due to close in late November, and then what? I was still in therapy and in a lot of pain. I had no car. We just bought Mat a brand-new car before all of this. I had no job and not a dime to my name! Grace was a junior in high school, and Michael a junior in college.

God gave me the strength to go on and the courage and wisdom to endure through this. I was determined to have some kind of work by the end of the week.

I was still in therapy with Larry. "Ann, how are you going to work during this?" he asked me.

"Larry, I will have to drag myself and just get through. With God's hand in mine, I can do anything."

By the end of that week, I had four jobs. First, I opened my own hair salon out of my house with no clients, but it was a start. Second, I returned to the hair salon I was working for before the accident Third, I got a job driving a golf cart full of drinks on the golf course for golfers. They would call me the "beer bitch," and I would get so mad. It was so degrading, but it was money. Now the fourth job to me was the worst. I was working as a waitress at a country club. I had never done this kind of work before. Some people were nice, but others were just so mean. Most of the time I was so tired when working. I was serving food, and I was so hungry! We would get in trouble if we ate anything. It paid bills and kept a roof over our heads. I just had to keep focused! I was working seven days a week and two jobs a day. I had to color-code the calendar to know where I was supposed to be and on what day. Sometimes I would change in the bathroom to go to the next job. One day I showed up at a job in the wrong outfit. I looked at my boss and said, "This is the best it gets today. Give me an apron please."

Even though I had no money, I was able to buy a used car on credit because I had credit established from previous cars we had leased or bought.

I sat down and figured out what I would need to meet the bills. I was overwhelmed.

Grace knew I was stressing out. "Mom, I can work too. I can help!"

"I love you, honey, but you just worry about school."

Thanksgiving came, and Mat was to move out that weekend but the paperwork delays things. The kids and I went to my mom's for the holiday. I had lost sixty pounds and was not eating much. I just had to keep going.

I was still getting therapy on my back with Larry. He knew the stress I was under, and he was always there for me. I think he kept me sane most of the time. He always knew what I need and when. Now Mary was back in my life, and we were quickly becoming great friends again. God always sends me what I need at the perfect time.

Two weeks later, Mat moved out. He didn't have any money for movers, so I found myself still fixing everything. "Mat, you rent a truck. And, Michael, you and I will move you. Truth of the matter is, I want him to go, but I am still trying to shut down the love in my heart for him despite everything. I told him I would give him half of the household furniture. I made sure he had everything to start a household even down to soap and toilet paper. I did not want to see him go without. We didn't have much, and what we did have wasn't great. But it was OK. There were few things that we argued over, but I was very fair to him. I told him most women would have thrown his clothes out on the lawn the first day. It was two weeks shy of a year that this had all started. It was time for him to go. Life was about to change.

Mat used to smoke but had quit for ten years. The minute he left, he lit up a cigarette and began to drink. I knew I had to stop doing things for him, stop caring for him, stop fixing his life.

Our first Christmas apart came. I tried to make it as normal as I could. I invited Mat over for Christmas morning so we could open presents together with Grace and Michael. It was so awkward. We had breakfast and opened presents. He thanked me for having him over. I felt relief when he left, just as if I could start my day now. We went to my mom's house with my family. A loud Christmas with lots of food. I was sitting next to my nephew and godson, who was also going through a divorce. We both were pretty low.

"Aunt Ann, you can't go any lower when you're at the bottom!"

I knew things were bad, but I just didn't feel that way. Things were hard, but I was not going to just lie down and roll over. I was doing everything I could to keep us afloat and repair what was left of my family.

New Year's Eve was just around the corner, and I had to work that night waitressing. I suggested to Mat that he invite Michael and Grace over for the night. I didn't know how this was supposed to work, so I was trying to find a new normal for all of us. Grace and Michael went to Mat's house just to find his gay friend Robert there. What a way to shatter the evening. When Grace and Michael came home the next day, they were very uncomfortable. They knew longer know who their dad was. The man he had been there whole life was different than who he was now. This person was a total stranger, and someone they really didn't like. I was angry with Mat for doing this so early on. I think this was the beginning of him destroying what was left of his relationship with the kids. I was still trying to fix things up, but now I was going to start backing off.

We got through the holidays, and I was working all the time. I still needed to work on my own mind. I went to church and prayed to God. "Please, my father in heaven, just show me some proof that he's gay, so I can close it down in my mind!" Well, be careful what you ask God for because he hears you and will answer you for sure.

I got a court date for the divorce hearing. I had to go by myself. I called my mom and told her. "Ann, you just hold your head up high. Honey, you'll be fine."

"I love you, Mom."

Mary called me. "Ann, do you want me to go with you?" She knew the pain of it all for she had just gone through the same thing not that very long ago.

"Thanks, Mary. I love you for that, but I'll be OK."

I thought, *OK, I'm going to look good for court if I have to do this alone.* It was a cold day in January. I put on my tight studded jeans with my black boots, my green leather coat with my burgundy scarf, and walked into court with my head held high. I was the first case to be heard. The judge called me up. Mat never showed up at all. Grace stayed with me. She was sixteen and had decided for herself. I got child support (but Mat ended up making only two payments, and I never saw another penny).

The judge looked at me and said, "Let me commend you for not having to use mediation and taking care of separating all of your belongings by yourself." I thanked the judge and was very impressed that he took the time to tell me that. It made me feel strong. I did what my mom told me to do. I walked out with my head held high. One tear ran down my cheek, and I quickly wiped it away. "Please, put my hand in yours, my lord, and don't let it go," I prayed.

Mary called to see if I was OK. We were becoming such good friends again.

Grace knew that I was going to court and was upset for me. She came home from school and asked how it went. I told her and she just hugged me.

I started the annulment that very day after I walked out of court. All the paperwork was ready. All I had to do was send it, but I had to be legally divorced in the state before I could start it.

About a month later, I called Janice, Mat's therapist, and asked her to meet with me. I know Mat had stopped going to her.

We sat down in her office, and she was slow to start. "Hello, Ann. How are you doing?"

"Janice, it's OK. I was the one who told you right up front he was gay."

There was a silence, and she looked away from me. I continued on, "It's not easy to see in him, is it?"

She quietly replied, "No, it isn't."

A knife slid right through my heart again. I didn't think it would hurt this much anymore. "Janice, I know this is a stupid question, but just how gay was he?"

"Ann, he is very high up there."

"Janice, I think you are the first person he has ever talked to about it. Why couldn't he just talk to me about it?

"Ann, because he's not ready to talk to you, and I don't know if he will ever be ready to. Maybe on his deathbed."

"Well, Janice, I won't need to hear it then."

"Ann, if you want to save this marriage, there is a group of people who work with people like Mat. You know why he won't touch you. He thinks you're his mother. He's got it all mixed up. His mother, his religion, his gay wants. He has split into two personalities."

I was not stunned by this because it's all starting to make sense to me. I was very calm. I was prepared to hear it. It still hurt very much. "No, Janice, it's three personalities," I said. Now that I could plug this in, I could see it so clearly.

The first one is the gay teenage boy crying in the closet. He's afraid and alone. The second one is one mean son of a bitch who hates the gay boy and everything else. The third one is the man I married. He molded himself after his dad and to what he thought the world wanted him to be. He never existed! It was all a lie. The help Mat needed was way above what I could help him with. He doesn't want help; he doesn't want to face it. I know Mat almost as well as God knows him, and I know he never will go back.

"As far as a marriage, Janice, there never was one here," I continued. "He was gay, and I am heterosexual. Two different herds of people. You can't change who you are. He has stolen my life because he couldn't face his own. He has robbed me of my youth and cheated me into having his children. Never did he tell me the truth or give me a choice. He had choices in his life and still chose to lie, cheat, steal and rob, and betray me. There never was a marriage here. Thank you for your help, Janice, but it's time for me to move on."

This was one of our last conversations. I didn't need any more.

Mary called me later that week. She understood all of this so well. She kept me sane most of the time.

As I processed all of this, life goes on! I kept fighting for happiness and "the new normal."

I was working so many hours it's crazy. Grace and I were still moving things to Mat's house. Stupid things that he forgot, but they're his, so I just want it done.

Mat kept calling and asking if he could come back to get some things off the computer. I didn't want him back in the house because I just don't trust him anymore. He couldn't quite tell me exactly what he needed, so once again, I smelled a rat. It still hurt to see him, and it's very uncomfortable for both Mat and me. I was not real computer savvy either, so I just kept putting him off.

I had a small break in my work schedule. I called Mat and told him that we needed to sit down, and he needed to tell me the truth about what happened. We met three days later at his house. He was in a very foul mood.

"Mat, I have been a faithful, loving wife to you for twenty-eight years. I deserve the truth from you."

He just sat there, twirling the corners of his mustache, just glaring at me.

He finally spoke!

"I NEVER WANTED YOU, ANN!"

This cut through me like a sword. To hear him say he never wanted me was to confirm how much he had betrayed me.

"I'm beginning to see that, Mat. You should have just never married. Why me?"

"Call it selfish. All I wanted was kids and a house."

"Well, Mat, there's a lot more to call it than selfish. So you stole my life, so you could have what you wanted."

"Ann, you need to go away and forget you ever knew me!"

"That's thirty years of my life, Mat, but I'm working on it."

I got up slowly and picked up my purse and left. My heart in my chest hurt so much. I was so betrayed, and I could now feel the sting of it so well.

I came home and called my mom. She tried once again to comfort me, but I was much too low.

I was trying very hard to find some normalcy again. The tension was gone in the house, so Grace and I were under less pressure. Michael came home when he had to but was busy with school.

My mom called me. She was very worried about me and how I was going to handle everything. "Ann, honey, sell your house and just move back with me."

"Mom, I love you, but I'll make it somehow."

Now Kyle had been calling about the lawsuit. "Ann, how are you doing?"

"I'm hanging in there, Kyle." He was divorced as well, so he knew the craziness of it all, and I knew he was lonely too.

"Ann, we need to get some medical records for our case."

"OK, sure, Kyle. I like to keep you up-to-date with all the therapy. I'll get you what you need." Kyle and I now talked about once every two weeks.

The house was still not finished, and I tried to take one problem at a time, but I was tired of living in a mess. Half-finished hardwood floors. No moldings up. Fireplace mantel wasn't done. Closet floors not finished. Window seals not finished, etc. We had done the kitchen, bathrooms, electrical, walls moved, plastering, repairing ceilings…I paid the builder in full to finish, but he has stopped everything since my divorce. Women alone get treated differently. I hate it! He told me he would finish some of the work for another $1,000.

"But I have paid you in full already."

"Well, you can either pay me to finish or get someone else."

"What choice do I have?" I was so mad. "You better be here to finish and then get out of my house."

He did come and finish the work. "Ann, you can pay me $100 a week if you want to because I know you don't have much money."

I handed him an envelope with $1,000 cash in it. "Your work is done here. I have paid you in full for the second time. I don't ever want to hear that I owe you anything again. Now please go."

"Ann, I didn't expect this. Is this cutting you short?"

"This will take food off my table, but I would rather you get out than eat right now. Please go!"

When he left, I made a list of everything that still needed to be done. It seemed like a lot, but I thought, *I'll take this one day at a time.*

Michael came home a week later for the weekend and for a break from college. I told him about the builder and what he did to me. "Michael, if you see this man even near this house, you stop him."

"What are you telling me, Mom, to get a baseball bat?"

"Yes, I am. He needs to go."

"OK, done, Mom."

I was getting rid of the stress in my life and it was hard, but I was making it. I was still going to therapy with Larry, working four jobs, trying to help Grace fit in at school, going through my annulment, doing all the housework by myself, going through the lawsuit with Kyle for the car accident, but I was doing it. With God's hand, In mine I am doing it. It is a fine line though.

CHAPTER 11

My Mom's Illness and Death

IT WAS THE MIDDLE OF February, and my sister Kathy called me. "Ann, I have some news for you."

"What's up, Kathy?"

"We've taken Mom to the hospital."

"What? Why?"

"For a month now, she has been complaining about pain in her back. And finally, she started crying. She never complains, so we have her at the hospital."

"I will be there in an hour."

I hung up the phone in a panic. I ran to my boss. "I'm leaving. My mom has been taken to the hospital. I'll call you when I know more."

He didn't say a word. He just nodded to go.

Running out the door, with my coat half on and my cell phone in one hand, I tried to get ahold of Grace. She's at school, but I knew she could answer between classes, so I kept ringing the phone. Finally she answered. "Hi, Mom."

"Grace, they have taken Grandma to the hospital. And I am on my way there now. I don't know when I'll be back. Are you going to be all right by yourself?"

"Mom, I'll be fine. Please call me and keep me informed."

"I will, honey. I'll call later."

I was driving fast as I could to get there. Finally, I was running into the ER to find my mom. Every crazy thought was going through my head. Finally, I found her and my sisters, Beth and Kathy.

"I'm here, Mom."

She looked at me with great pain in her eyes. Kathy gave me a little update. "They are coming with a shot of strong pain medicine, morphine I think, to take the edge of pain off. Mom hasn't slept in two days."

My sister Karen walked in. She got a quick update too. They gave my mom the shot, and she fell asleep in fifteen minutes. The doctors now had to start tests to see what was wrong. For the next seven hours, we were in the ER, but finally, they let us take her home.

Kathy, Beth, and Karen lived close to my mom, but Jean lived out of state and I lived an hour away. Now that my mom was stable for the moment, I had to go home. Grace was alone, and I had to work tomorrow. I couldn't miss a beat.

The next week was a series of doctors and medical tests. Finally, the decision was made. Kathy had medical power of attorney, so she really took charge. The doctors said my mother needed a quadruple bypass for her heart. Now my mom was seventy-seven years old, but in good health. Surgery was scheduled for that week.

Jean flew in for the surgery. I was still really angry with her for going to lunch with Mat and butting in. None of my sisters had really been supportive through all of this, so I just wanted to help my mom and stay by myself. My voice was really not heard when we're all together anyway.

I took off the day of surgery. Grace wanted to come, but I told her no. I didn't know when I'll be home.

My mother called me and my sisters into the room before they took her into surgery. "Now if something happens to me in surgery, I want all of you to stick together."

I didn't even want to think of a world without my mom. The medical staff kept coming in with needles, and it made me sick to my stomach. I had to walk out. I felt as if I was going to pass out. I went down the hall to sit down, and I could hear my sister Beth being mean to me, telling everyone how weak I was and such a baby. Beth had always had a cruel streak in her.

They wheeled my mom away. I caught one last glimpse of her, and I mouthed to her, "I love you." She saw me and smiled. For the next six hours, I prayed quietly and wait.

Finally surgery was over and now for the recovery. I told Kathy I was going home, and I'll be back soon. "OK, Ann," she said. "Be careful going home." I felt that my mother was on her way to recovery.

Kathy called the next day. "Ann, Mom is not coming out of the anesthesia very well. Can you come and stay one day?"

"Yes, I can get the day off tomorrow. I will be there at 5:00 a.m."

"Great."

I told Grace I had to go to the hospital to help Grandma. "Mom," she told me, "Dad keeps calling me, but I don't want to talk to him. He's starting to creep me out."

"Honey, if you want to talk with your dad, you have a phone, a computer, a car, and the mail. He is not allowed in this house, and I don't want him to know my business. You and Michael are old enough to make your own relationship with him whatever that may be. If you don't want to speak to him, don't. I have to worry about working and Grandma right now. You need to worry about getting into college."

The next morning I was at the hospital at 5:00 a.m. I stood outside my mom's door like a scared child. A nurse was with her. He came out to talk to me. "Is this your mom?"

"Yes."

"You can come in."

"I'm afraid to. I'm not great with needles."

"Well, just come in slow."

"OK." He slowly coaxed me into the room. I saw my mom's face in the shadows of the nightlight. I talked to her quietly. "Hi, Mom, it's Ann."

She stirred a little. "I love you, Mom!"

She tried to answer back, but she was really slurring her words. I asked the nurse, "Has she had a stroke?"

"No, she is still waking up."

"But it's been two days."

"I know. Some people take a week."

"Wow. What can I do to help?"

"Just talk to her and maybe rub her softly."

"OK."

Her numbers on the monitor were not good. I started talking to her. "Mom, I'm right here, and I'm staying as long as I can." I started to rub her head softly. I kept talking. "I said a rosary for you. The Lord is here with you. Grace and Michael send their love. I love you." I kept rubbing her head.

The nurse said, "What are you doing?"

"I'm just talking and rubbing her head. Am I hurting her?"

"No! No! Look at how good her numbers on the monitor are. Keep doing it."

"OK."

"Your sister was here yesterday, and they were horrible."

"Which sisters?"

"Jean and Beth."

"I'm sorry. They tend to be a bit of a pain in the butt. Let's just get these numbers better for my mom."

The nurse asked me to stay longer because my mother was responding so well. "I will stay as long as you let me," I told him. I stayed for four hours just rubbing her head and telling her we loved her. I called Kathy and let her know how well Mom was doing.

A week later, we moved her home to recover. Jean left for home. Things seemed good.

I was working so much I could hardly come up for air. Sometimes I only have $5 in my purse and just to get out. Grace and I went to a restaurant and ordered one order of French fries and split them. It's a good time to talk. Michael came home from college with his friends for chili night. They loved it.

My therapy was coming to an end soon with Larry, and I knew our time together will stop. We would have to let go of each other. He once said to me, "Ann, I have learned more from you than I have ever learned in thirty-five years of therapy." I have leaned on him as much, but it was time to sail on. Larry picked me up off the floor when no one else would! I was going to miss him.

Now Mary and I have become great friends again. It seemed like Larry was leaving, and Mary was taking over. We both have gone through the same betrayal by men. She was a lot like me in many ways. When I think I'm crazy, she assures me that I'm not. We talked on the phone almost daily now. It's nice to have someone to go through hard times with. I didn't feel so alone anymore.

My mom was staying home and recovering from surgery. She still looked very pale and in pain a lot. A little at a time...I talked to her daily and visit when I could.

Mat wanted to see Grace and Michael, but he kept getting stranger and stranger. He kept calling Grace, but I think she didn't know how to feel. She really just wanted to be left alone right now. Being a junior in high school, she had a lot of college prep to do.

I called my mom this morning. "Hi, Mom, how are you feeling today?"

"I'm sore, and my back hurts."

"Just take your time and rest today, Mom. Don't push yourself."

"Ann, you have a letter here from the Archdiocese of the Church."

"Wow, that was quick. Just put it aside, Mom, and I will get it when I come to see you later this week. I love you, Mom!"

"I love you too, honey."

I had to meet with Kyle tomorrow, and his office was right by my mom's house. This will save me some time, and I will get to see my mom.

I went to Kyle's office first. We were in his office, and I was talking about the case to him. He's looking at me like I'm a pork chop and he's a Doberman. I stopped talking to him for a moment and then I said to him, "Oh my god, you think I'm hot!"

He got a big cocky smile on his face. Kyle had salt-and-pepper hair and a mustache. He had brown eyes and a medium build. He's a little disheveled for a lawyer. "Why, yes I do, Ann," he said.

"Kyle, we are in the middle of business together. Now focus."

"All right, all right."

"I think we're done here today, Kyle. I'm going to see my mom."

I got to my mom's house, and the door was open.

"Hi, Mom."

"Hi, honey."

Now it's about three weeks after her surgery, and her wounds were starting to heal over. She handed me the letter from the Archdiocese. It just told me that they were reviewing my case. *OK, I'm ready.* Father Jim had become my advocate before the tribunal. I was so thankful for him. Someday I will thank him.

My mom and I visited for a while, but then I had to go. I called my sister Kathy on the way home. "How does Mom look to you, Kathy?"

"Well, she's still recovering, Ann, so we have to give her time."

"OK, Kathy, I'll be patient."

Mat called the house later that week, and he wanted access to our computer again. I couldn't figure out what he wanted, but I told him this time that I had work done on the computer, and they erased a lot of things to give me more room. He seemed to sigh in relief. He asked about my mom. I really didn't want him to know my business anymore. I felt like he was a cancer in my life now, and I just wanted to cut him out so I could heal.

I was working ten solid days in a row and two jobs a day. I called my mom on my breaks or lunch. Grace and I were like ships passing in the night sometimes; and Michael, well, I saw him once a month for about an hour.

Grace had to have her wisdom teeth out. It's cold outside, and my furnace had broken. I was trying to keep the house warm, but it's going to take two days for the part to come in.

This was a heavy snowstorm starting as Grace was getting her teeth out. I had an hour drive to get home. She came out and looked bad. "Come on, honey. I'll take you home."

I put her in the car and wrapped a blanket around her. The snow was coming down hard and it's slippery out. My cell phone rang, and I had to answer it because it's the man doing the furnace for us. I was doing seventy miles an hour and trying to tell him the part number he needed, and Grace told me she's going to throw up.

"Stick your head out the window," I yelled. "I'll pull off the expressway."

I hung up on the furnace man. I pulled into a parking lot, and Grace vomited all over herself. I got her out of the car, and she vomited again. She started to cry. I sat down on the pavement. The snow was coming so hard that we looked like snowmen. There's vomit all over, Grace was crying, and I just started laughing out loud. I was laughing so hard that Grace started to laugh too.

"Mom, you're crazy."

"Yes, I am, Grace. Yes, I am…Do you feel better now, honey?"

"Yes."

"OK, let's clean you up and go home."

When we got home, the house was cold, and the heat won't be fixed for another day. I got Grace to the couch and bundled her up with pillows and blankets. "Just sleep now," I told her. "I was going to try to buy a space heater to keep us warm. Tonight we'll both sleep in my bed. We could stay warm that way, and I could keep an eye on you."

"OK, Mom. Mom?"

"Yes, honey?"

"Thanks for taking care of me."

"You're welcome, honey. You take care of people, especially the ones you love."

She fell asleep. I came back with the heater and it helped. We stayed warm all night by the grace of God.

My mom called to check on us the next day. "How are things going, Ann?"

"Better today, Mom. We have heat again, and Grace is feeling better. I have to work till late, so I'm getting ready now. How are you feeling, Mom?"

"Well, my back still hurts. Surgery is rough."

"Maybe you need to heal some more yet. It's still early,"

"I guess."

"I'll be over in a few days, Mom, and I'll give you a soft massage. Maybe that will help."

"Sounds good, honey."

Two days went by. Kathy called me early in the morning before I went to work. "Good morning, my sister!"

"Hi, Ann. Listen, Mom still is having a great deal of pain in her back, and it's two months after her surgery."

"I know, Kathy."

"What do you think?"

"I think she needs some tests done. The doctor is ordering blood work to start."

"Well, please keep me posted."

"Sure I will."

"We'll talk later."

It's going to be a long day today. I started work at 6:30 a.m. I would work three jobs: hair at home then the beer cart, change in bathroom, and go to the country club to waitress. I wouldn't be home until 4:00 a.m. tomorrow. Sometimes I was so tired and sore that I got sick to my stomach. I just focused on the hour in front of me. My injuries from the car accident sometimes get in the way. Sometimes my back swells into my lungs and it's hard to breathe, but there is a drug for everything. I just pushed forward.

Mat really wanted to see Grace and Michael, but they're not interested in seeing him. He asked Grace to come and live with him. She loved her dad, but the dad she knew was gone! She did not care for this person that was left. Mat treated Michael and Grace so differently. With Michael, he seemed to do the minimum. With Grace, he was obsessive. He wanted to tie her to his hip and never let her go, and Grace was very aware of all of this. She hated how he treated Michael. I had warned Grace before we were divorced that Mat would want her to live with him. I tried to prepare her so she could think about it and answer from her heart. "Honey, I love you, and this is your home. But if you want to live with your dad, you're old enough to make that decision by yourself."

She was ready when he asked her to answer him from her heart. "No, thank you, Dad. I'm going to stay with Mom for now. I just want to finish high school."

Kathy called this morning. Her voice was low. "Ann, Mom's blood work is back."

"OK and—"

"And she has bone cancer."

"WHAT! How did they miss this?"

"Well, this is a secondary cancer. We don't know where the primary cancer is coming from."

I fell silent. After seeing my father die from cancer, I knew this was not going to be good.

"Ann, Ann, are you there?"

"Yes, Kathy. How bad are we talking?"

"Well, more tests have to be done, but it's not good."

"I have to go, Kathy, but we'll talk later."

I was very quiet. I got dressed for work and left. I stopped in the church first. As I knelt down, I was humbled before God. "My father in heaven, I love you and thank you for all you give me. But please, Father, let this cup pass my mother. I don't think I can take another brick on my shoulders, especially this. I can handle everything but not this. Please let there be a miracle here." I dried my tears that had fallen on the floor, and I left for work.

My mind was not on work at all that night. People were talking to me, and I didn't even hear them. My heart reopened the wounds that were starting to heal a little, but now a different kind of wound twice as big.

When I wake the next morning, I had a talk with Grace, and I told her about her grandma, whom she adored. The big C word (cancer) had come once again to the house. Later that day, I called Michael and told him. Just when things seem to be going better, the next bend in the river came, and this was a bad one.

The next three weeks brought more results from testing. The primary source of cancer was coming from her breast, and it had metastasized to her bones already. I'm sure the heart surgery accelerated all of this. I continued to pray, "Father, please hear my prayer. I know that she belongs in heaven with you, because she is an angel, but please don't take her from me."

Mary called me daily now, and sometimes two or three times a day.

My friend Dana had lost her mom about three years ago and understood the pain of it all.

Mat had found out somehow about my mom too. He called to ask about her. I really didn't want him to know any of my business. I really wish he would just go away and leave us alone. It's so much to deal with him too.

Kathy called. (She is my mom's health executor by living trust.) Beth, Jean, and Karen didn't even bother calling anymore. "Ann, the cancer has gone too far, and Mom is seventy-seven. Putting her through chemo was a lot of pain for something they couldn't stop. The cancer was even in the fluid around her brain."

"How long does she have, Kathy?"

"From what I can see, a year to a year and a half."

Even though there were five of us children, my voice was never heard. This was the best choice we had at the time. They were going to give her drugs to strengthen her bones because the cancer would eat them away. This may help a little.

It seemed as though God had answered me. There would be *no* miracle this time. My mother was going to die soon. God did answer our prayers but not always the way we want him to. He doesn't promise us a great life here on earth, but he does promise never to leave us.

I called Michael and gave him the news. Grace and I talked when she came home from school and me from work. I knew they were hurting, and I was trying to be strong, but my heart was bleeding from pain.

I had to call my mom and try to put a brave face on for her. I did my crying when I'm alone. "Hi, Mom."

"Hi, honey."

"I'm sorry, Mom, for your illness."

"What are you going to do, Ann? You have to deal with what comes."

"I know, Mom, but I'm working so many jobs. And I just want to care for you, but my hands are tied. I'm angry with Mat for doing this to us."

"I know, honey. One day at a time."

"I love you, Mom."

"I love you too, honey."

Several weeks passed. My mom's treatments were going OK. She got a little sick from them but was holding her own. I called her between jobs several times a day. I tried to see my mom at least once a week. I could see her failing though.

Michael came home for a month before he left for his summer job, which is out of state. He brought all of his college stuff back, and it was everywhere. I couldn't keep up anymore. The house looked to be in ruins. (I hate that.) I had to lay a new basement floor, which means taking the old tile up and laying new tile. This was between jobs and seeing my mom.

We were all getting home for the evening and talking for five minutes.

"Michael, Grace, we are going to do the basement floor together."

"Mom, are you crazy!" Michael yelled.

"Maybe I am, but it has to be done, and we can do it if we work together. We only have a short time to finish. We'll start chipping the old stuff out tomorrow. If we can lay thirty new tiles a night, we could finish it before you leave, Michael."

"Are you sure you want to do this, Mom?" Michael asked.

"Well, no, but it needs to be done. I have an hour before I go to work tomorrow, so we start tomorrow."

"Oh my god, Mom, fine!"

The next day, as tired as I am, I dragged myself out of bed early to start. Of course, Michael and Grace were in sleeping comas. I left lists for them to do so we could stay on schedule. At first it was good, but then I start coming home and nothing was done. I got so mad at Michael and Grace. I just kept going though. It was almost mind-numbing, therapeutic if you will. I chipped out old tile for one hour before the day started and then Michael did an hour. It was hard work, but my arms were looking great. Every day I started work and I was so sore.

Mary kept saying, "Ann, how are you doing all of this?"

"By the grace of God, Mary."

I guess I didn't want to feel all the pain I was in, so I stayed so busy I didn't have time to think. Grace, Michael, and I lay thirty tiles a night when I come home from work. Well into the night, we glued tiles to the floor. My knees were toast. One night they made me stay over at work, and I was not going to be able to tile. I called Grace, and I was so upset.

"Don't worry, Mom. We'll get it done soon."

When I came home from work that night, Grace and Michael have laid all the tiles for me so I could just rest. I was so thankful to them. We finished the floor in time. Michael left for his job for the summer. Grace was working and going into her senior year of high school. She had to take her senior pictures this summer. She was applying to colleges as well.

"Mom, please come with me for my pictures."

"Grace, I'll have to get a day off work."

"Please, Mom!"

"OK, fine. I'll fit it in somewhere."

I was almost afraid to ask for it off. I've had to ask for so much time off already. I didn't know how much my bosses will tolerate. I guessed you just have to weigh your priorities and be honest with them, and do your best.

The summer flew by. I tried to see my mom at least once every two weeks, but I talked with her at least three times a day. I just wanted to spend more time with her, but I was the sole support of a teenager I was raising alone. I knew time was growing short, though, for my mom.

Mat kept trying to see Michael and Grace. They kept avoiding him like the black plague. I thought they were still processing the whole mess. It's going to take a long time to heal my family. How long, I'm not sure, but I think it will be longer than I thought—a lot longer.

"OK, Grace and Michael, do you want to see your dad?" I asked them.

Grace spoke up first. "I don't know, Mom. He's different now, and he creeps me out."

"And how about you, Michael?"

"I really don't want to see him, Mom."

"Well, you guys need to tell him. He thinks I'm keeping you from him. You're both old enough to make your own decisions about your relationship with your father." I stopped and thought to myself, I didn't have to fix this anymore. Mat caused this mess. He would have to fix his own life. I had to move on.

Michael left for college. This was his senior year. A very busy year for him. Grace started her senior year in high school. She had her senior pictures back and was busy with college apps. She hated her school but had tried to adapt. I worked so much that I hardly had time to notice. I needed my Grace to be strong now. She had to be older than her years.

Kathy called. "Hi, Ann. We have a problem."

"Oh no. Now what, Kathy?"

"Mom is getting too bad to be left alone. We need twenty-four-hour care now. I will hire people for the daytime, but we will have to take turns at night."

"Kathy, you, Beth, and Karen all live ten minutes from Mom, and you all have husbands. I'm an hour one way, and I'm all alone with Grace out here. We don't know anyone out here to help, and I need to work to pay the bills. I live from paycheck to paycheck right now. How can I do that?"

"Well, Ann, do what you can do."

"My hands are tied right now, Kathy. If I get a day off, I'll come and help."

"OK, Ann. We'll talk later."

I feel backed into a corner right now. All I wanted was to take care of my mom, but money was a big problem right now, and I couldn't leave Grace alone out here.

The next day Beth called. "Ann, why can't you spend the night with Mom one night a week?"

"Beth, I work seven days a week, two jobs a day, and I'm out here alone with Grace. I can't just leave her alone."

"Why can't she go with her dad?"

"Well, Beth, if it is any of your business, Grace is uncomfortable with him. This is her home, and I won't make things any worse for her. There are only so many hours in the day, and I have no time for anything. The winter is upon us and getting through the storms is going to be hard. There are three of you. You will have to rotate for now."

"I don't believe you have four jobs, Ann!"

"Well, Beth, I do. And I don't have to prove anything to you."

The phone hung up. Beth had always loved to control everything and everyone, but not this time. I had no choice.

I called my mom, and I talked to her. "Mom, I love you very much, and all I want to do is take care of you, but my life is not my own right now. I am only one person, and there are only so many hours in a day to work and pay bills. There is no one to help, Mom. I get so angry at Mat for putting us in this position. I still have to keep a roof over our heads and food on the table. I can't leave Grace alone, and this is a big year for her. She can't miss school."

"Ann, don't worry. It's OK. We'll figure out something."

"You shouldn't have to worry about this stuff, Mom. You're so sick and you should be resting, and I can't even help you, Mom. I'm so sorry, and I'll do what I can."

"I understand, honey."

The pressure right now was horrible. My injuries in my back from the car accident kept swelling up because I work long hours and I lifted too much. It took time for the swelling to go down, but there wasn't enough time between jobs for that to happen, so I had a hard time breathing because they put pressure on my lungs. I had a talk with my boss at the country club about it. I explained to him that I couldn't work till 4:00 a.m. and go to another job by 9:00 a.m. the same day. I was only one person, and I needed sleep too. I couldn't work if I couldn't breathe. He cut my hours a little to help.

Now Kyle needed me to come in for work on the lawsuit. He was at least close to my mom.

I called Kathy to tell her I could help that day with my mom. I tried to give everyone a break and help Mom. Her mind was very sharp, but she was very unsteady on her feet. I cooked for her and helped her get to the bathroom and whatever she needed. It's time for me to go, and Beth came in. She was still telling me I had to come at least one night.

"Beth, I have Grace at home alone. I work and I have a dog. What do you want me to do?"

"Well, leave Grace with her dad."

"Beth, Grace is very uncomfortable with Mat right now, and I am not going to force her to do that. She needs to concentrate on school and just be a teenager. She has been under enough stress in our house for a lifetime."

"I don't care, Ann. You need to do this."

"Well, Beth, thank you for your advice on what I should do. Mom, I'm going to go. I'll call later."

Now the holidays were upon us. This was the first Thanksgiving without Mat, and I just wanted to be with Grace and Michael and my mom. Mat wanted the kids with him, but they didn't want to go with him. I didn't know how much time we had left with my mom, so I really wanted to be with her this holiday season. Grace had told me that she and Michael were going with me.

Beth was really mean to me, Grace, and Michael all Thanksgiving Day. Karen was not much better to us. I was trying real hard to hold on to the joy in my heart and not let anyone or anything ruin my time that day. By the time it's time to go, I was ready to leave. My sisters had been just so mean to me and my kids for no reason at all. At night I sat on the edge of my bed in the dark staring at the night sky looking for the peace of God! Looking for the one whom I know loved me and would never leave me. I fell asleep and saw him in my dreams with his arms around me.

A week later, Mat called me. He was really nice. He asked me to get stuff off the computer again. I knew something was hidden there, but what? I brushed him off again. Two days later, I had to look up a website for one of my jobs. I was so bad on the computer. I just started pushing buttons until I figured it out. On this particular day, I pushed the wrong button, which opened the old history to the computer. As I started reading, I was appalled to find gay porn websites that I never knew about. Another knife right through my heart. I ran upstairs to Grace's bedroom.

"Grace, do you know about this stuff I found on the computer?"

"Mom, what have you found?"

"Several gay porn sites!"

"That's been on there since before we moved, Mom."

"Honey, you knew about this?!"

"Yes."

"I am so angry with your dad right now." I grabbed the phone and dialed Mat's phone.

He answered the phone. "Hi, Ann."

"You rat-ass bastard!"

"What's wrong?"

"You will never stop lying to me, Mat, will you? I have found your gay porn websites on the computer. The ones you have been looking to erase before I found them! Well, Mat, I think I'm going to print them up and send them in Christmas cards to your family."

"I'll do whatever I want to do, Ann."

"You need help, Mat. Lots of help."

I hung up the phone. I was so mad I was shaking. Grace watched all of this. I worry about the toll this was taking on her. All I knew was I wanted Mat to disappear from our lives. Christmas was going to be real lean this year, but this may be my last Christmas with my mom.

Dec. 16 came, and I had the flu. I was throwing up and my stomach hurt. I couldn't stay out of the bathroom. I just want to lie on the couch. I was missing so much work. I couldn't go near my mom. God help me if I gave her anything more to deal with.

It's now Christmas morning, and I was still sick. "Grace and Michael, you have to go to Grandma's without me. I can't go near Grandma like this," I told them. "I am too weak now. Nothing is moving except for my eyeballs, and even that hurts. You guys go and tell Grandma I love her."

"OK, Mom. We'll bring you some food."

I wanted to go so badly, but I could not put my mom in danger. Grace and Michael returned a few hours later.

"How was it?"

"We had fun with our cousins, but Aunt Beth and Aunt Karen were very mean to us, and Aunt Jean wasn't much better. The only one besides Grandma that was nice was Aunt Kathy."

"Did you tell them I was sick?"

"Yes, Mom, and they didn't care."

"I'll call Grandma tomorrow and explain, Grace."

"There was no reason for it, Mom."

"Just let it go, Grace. I don't have the energy right now to think about it."

The next day I called my mom and Karen answered. She told me my mom was in the bathroom, and she couldn't talk to me. "Karen, just have Mom call me when she's done."

"Fine, Ann!"

I called three more times, and my sisters would not let me talk to my mom. Finally I was so sick I told Michael and Grace I needed to go to the ER. I called my mom one more time to let her know I was going to the ER. One of my nieces answered.

"Hi, honey. Please just tell Grandma that I will be at the ER, and I will call when I can."

"OK, Aunt Ann."

Grace and Michael got me ready to go, and the phone rang. Grace answered. "Mom, it's Grandma."

"Wow, is that all it took was to go to the ER?" I picked up the phone. "Hi, Mom."

"Ann, what's wrong?"

"I don't know, but I'm dehydrating. I've been fooling with this for ten days now. It's time for the ER."

"Call me when you get home, honey."

"Are they going to let me talk to you, Mom?"

"Yes, they will."

"I'm sorry about Christmas, Mom. I so wanted to be there with you."

"Yes, I know, honey. Just worry about getting better right now."

Grace and Michael packed me up and took me to the ER. It felt so weird because I had always taken care of them and now they were taking care of me. It's hard to be alone and sick, at least I had my kids. They started an IV right away while they ran some tests. Six hours later, the doctor came in and told me I had food poisoning and that I was dehydrated, but he thought that most of it had run its course. They rehydrated me with IVs, put me on meds, and sent me home to rest. I was so afraid it was the flu, and I was going to give it to my mom that I missed Christmas with her, but food poisoning! It was probably from carrot juice or chicken.

I called my mom when I got home, and my sisters allowed her to talk to me. I told her I would be over in a week now that I knew I'm not contagious. I felt like I had missed Christmas.

A few weeks went by, and Beth called me again and was really being mean to me. "Ann, you have to take one night with Mom."

"Beth, how am I going to do that?"

"I don't care, Ann, how you do it. Just do it."

"OK, Ann. I will try one night a week and see how it goes." I really wanted to help my mom, but I couldn't stand to even talk to Beth anymore.

When I saw Grace that night, I told her that I was going to spend one night with Grandma to help, but she would have to stay alone.

"Mom, if it will help Grandma, I'll do it."

"Grace, I'm not really OK with this, but I don't know what else to do. We'll take it one day at a time."

I worked two jobs and drove to my mom's house at night. Now my mom gets frightened at night, so she doesn't sleep well; therefore, we're both up all night. I didn't mind if it made her feel better. The problem was next day when I went back to work. Just driving an hour was dangerous because I was falling asleep at the wheel. I kept smacking myself in the face and the radio was on full blast. The windows were all down, and it's twenty-five degrees out. When I got to work, I was on autopilot. *Oh god, how am I going to keep this pace up?* I've worried about Grace all night by herself. I was so glad Michael's in college, but I could use him about now.

The days continued on, and I was really dragging. As I came home today, I noticed the front door was not right. It had a screen door with glass. As I looked closer, the window was coming off the door right out of the frame. How was I going to fix this? The cold air was just pouring in, and anyone could break in, and Grace was here alone sometimes. I've got to fix this. I got out of the house early the next day and ran to Home Depot before work, I explained the problem to the salesperson. "Ma'am, there is no way to fix this. You need a whole new door."

"Well, I can't quite afford that now. I'll be back."

I went to work with a heavy heart. "Father in heaven, how am I going to pay for this? I can't see anymore, but you can. Please help me, Father."

I had to go spend the night at my mom's tonight. I walked out of work to go, and there was a terrible snowstorm. Visibility was about 20 percent, and it's icy. I was so afraid of another car accident. The roads were very bad. Car accidents everywhere, and I hadn't even started to her house. *I can't do this today! I just can't!!!* I called Kathy.

"Kathy, it's Ann."

"Hi, Ann."

"I just can't get through this storm today. I'm so sorry to leave you in this position, but I can't even see out here. You will have to call Karen or Beth or go yourself tonight to stay with Mom. Please tell her I'm sorry, but I am trying. I need to find Grace and head home."

"Ann, calm down."

"Well, Kathy, I knew this would happen when I started spending the night with Mom, and I hate to let everyone down, but I have to live today because my kids need me."

"It's OK. I'll figure it out. You just get home safely."

"Thanks, Kathy."

It's a white-knuckle ride all the way home. I was shaking when I got there. I knew all my sisters were mad at me, but I could not take another car accident. I had left Grace far too much on her own.

Grace came home finally. "Oh my god, Mom. My car almost slipped off the road three times…Wait, why are you home? Aren't you supposed to be at Grandma's?"

"Yes, but look at the storm. What do you think?"

"I know, Mom, it's wicked out. Is everyone mad at you?"

"Yes, and I'm sure Aunt Beth and Aunt Karen and Aunt Jean are all going to have something to say about it. And it won't be nice…Well, we're home safe tonight. Maybe I can get a solid night of sleep. That would be nice."

The next morning, I woke up, and the storm was winding down some. There were accidents everywhere. In my heart, I knew it was time to call my mom and talk to her.

"Good morning, Mom. How are you feeling?"

"Not great. I didn't sleep real good last night."

"I'm sorry, Mom. I just cannot make it through to your house in the winter. I will be back in April to help. I feel terrible, Mom. I know you need help."

"Don't worry, honey. I know it's hard for you. By the way, Ann, I have a letter from the Archdiocese for your annulment."

"I have been waiting for one. It has been a long time. Just put it aside, and I'll get it the next time I'm there. I'll call Kathy and tell her, Mom."

"OK, Ann."

I was getting late for my first job of the day! Not that I even care right now, but I was more like a robot when I got there. I just kept my head down and worked. When I got my first break, I called Kathy.

"Hi, Kathy."

"I know already, Ann. Mom told me."

"I knew this would happen, Kathy. How crazy mad are Beth, Karen, and Jean?"

"Well, they are very mad. Beth just hung up on me."

"Wow! I will try to get through when the weather is better. Until then, I am doing the best that I can."

"I know, Ann."

"I have to get back to work, Kathy. We'll talk later."

The winter was a treacherous one. Ice and snow up the yin-yang. I missed work several days because it was so bad. It was hard to keep up with the bills with heat and all. Mat had only paid one or two child support payment for Grace and then stopped paying at all. I could have chased him for it, but I did not have the time nor the money for a lawyer. I made a heat pack, which you microwaved for heat just to help stay warm, for Grace and I. Sometimes we would sleep in the same bed to stay warmer at night. I had to fix the front door, and I couldn't wait any longer. I could buy it on payments. The new door was beautiful and very energy efficient. The house looked better already.

In one of my jobs, I worked with food. One night the chef told a worker to throw a whole pan of chicken breasts away. It hadn't even been touched. I walked over and started to pack the food away to take home with me. The chef came over and said, "You cannot have that."

I became very serious. "A minute ago you were throwing this out, and now that I want it to feed my family with, you tell me I can't have it. Well, chef, that is a sin! To take food and throw it out when people can eat it and feed their children! I am taking this home so either fire me or walk away!"

He stared at me for a while and then walked away. I packed it up and took it home and made five different meals out of it. I should have been fired that night, but by the grace of God once again, I was not.

I called my mother three to four times a day just to hear her voice. Beth, Jean, and Karen were treating me like dirt. I had no voice in my mother's care. All I could do was try.

It was now breaking into spring, and winter was moving on.

There's always a renewed spirit on the earth in spring. The days are brighter, the flowers are coming out, the leaves on the trees are being born, and the warmth is returning.

Grace had been accepted to several colleges, and high school graduation was near. Michael's graduation from college was also coming. I was so proud of them both. Michael received partial scholarships, partial loans, and the rest he worked for. We could pay nothing, but he got himself through.

My mother was getting worse. Karen, Beth, and Jean were becoming very mean not only toward my mom, but Kathy and me as well.

Kathy called me. "Ann, Mom can't stay in her home anymore."

"Kathy, Mom can live with me. I will take care of her. I will take a leave of absence from my jobs, and Grace and I will take of her."

"Well, that's one option, Ann. Beth said Mom is going there. She is moving her to her house and that's that."

"OK, well, what does Mom want?"

"I guess she's OK with that."

"Well, Kathy, I guess there's nothing more to say. I will be free to come back soon, but if she's at Beth's house, Beth will be right there."

"I don't know how this is going to work out, but one day at a time, Ann."

"OK, let me know."

Now my mom was getting tired of being sick, and she was growing weaker as the cancer spread, but her mind was solid as a rock. Every day, it brought me closer to her not being there, a thought I could not bear!

The next day I talked with my mom, and she confirmed that she would be living with Beth. She seemed at peace. I felt she was comforted in the fact that she didn't have to worry about the house and her care anymore. Everything was set to move her by the end of the week. Three days later, Beth told my mom she could not move in with her with no real explanation.

My mother was crushed by this. Almost as if she had been thrown out in the streets by her own daughter. She was sick right now; she should not have to worry about this. It killed me to watch this. Kathy called to tell me we had to change the plan. Beth was growing into someone I didn't know.

I called my mom once again and offered to come out and care for her; but Karen, Jean, and Beth had convinced her that I would not take her to the doctors. My mom was scared now and felt alone right now, and she bought into the fear they had planted in her. I could not undo what they had done.

Everyone came up with their own plan. Jean, who lives out of state, told my mom that she could live with her for six months. In my mind, I thought of how horrid it was to put a time limit on your dying mother's head. Next was Kathy who told my mother that she would allow her to build a room off the back of her house and move into it. Her house is small, but this was going to be some bucks for my mom. She had enough to build the room and it's her money. She just didn't know what to do. At least it was an option. Then it was Karen's turn. Karen was one hot mess. She didn't have a house right now, and became very cold to my mom. Not an option. My turn. I once again tell my mom: Please move here. I promise you will want for nothing. My house was all one level and had nice views outside.

Grace and I will take care of you, Mom. Don't worry. Last and the very least in my mind was Beth, and we already knew her option or lack of one.

So there it was. All that was left for my mom in her dying days. A few sorry options. A mother who raised us with all she had to give. The love of God came through her to us always. She deserved so much more. At the very least to be at peace.

Kathy presented these options to my mom when they were alone. My mom chose to build the room off Kathy's house. I tried my best to comfort her fears about coming to my house and stepping up to the plate, but she felt better about building the room.

It was a very big undertaking for Kathy to hire people and get it built quickly.

In the meantime, Grace chose a college and was leaving to start in the summer. I could not have a party for either one of them, but I couldn't just let it go by with nothing. I saved my money to take Michael and Grace to a nice dinner to celebrate. In the midst of such turmoil, a little happiness was very welcome.

Michael's graduation was first! He studied pre-med and biology and was thinking of med school now. Grace and I drove to the college campus for the ceremony. It was an awful day. Dark skies. It was cold and rainy, and it was held outdoors on the lawn in the middle of campus. It just wasn't going to spoil my day though. Grace and I cheered for Michael and can't be any prouder. Things were going great. The ceremony was over, and we went to catch up to Michael. All of a sudden, Mat appeared! I was mortified. How dare he show up and ruin our day. I became very angry.

"Michael, I will meet you back in your room." I turned and abruptly walked away. How did he know the time and day? Who was telling him? I was pretty sure my mom told my sisters and they told Mat. I just know it!

Grace came running after me. "Mom, wait up! Mom, how did Dad know?"

"I don't know, Grace. Let's get Michael, pack him up, and go home."

We started for home. I asked, "Michael, did you invite your dad?"

"No, Mom. I don't know how he found out."

"Well, never you mind. It was a great day, honey."

The room for my mom was being built at record speed. It is Mother's Day, and Kathy and I had pitched in and bought beautiful linens and a quilted spread for her hospital bed. It is so much cheerier looking. I had beautiful lace curtains for her bright yellow room. It was going to be nice and light.

My mom called me. "Ann, are you going to have a party for Grace's graduation?"

"I have already talked to her about it, Mom. I just can't afford it right now. She understands."

"You could have it here."

"It's OK, Mom. Somewhere down the road, I'll make it up to her. Mom, have there been any more letters for me from the Archdiocese?"

"I don't know. Beth had all my mail rerouted to her house."

"Why? You can still read your own mail, Mom…I'll call her, Mom, and tell her to look for it. I've got to go to work a little early today so I can ask for the graduation day off."

"OK, honey."

"I love you, Mom."

As the week went on, Michael left for a summer job out of state. He would miss Grace's graduation, so that left me. The day arrived. and this time it's indoors. Thank you, God! I knew a few parents there, and they were kind enough to let me sit with them. I now had lost sixty-five pounds and was looking pretty good. As I was sitting waiting for things to start, I saw Mat in the upper balcony. Oh my god, not again! How was this rat infiltrating my life again? I spotted Grace in the lower level coming toward me. I went to the rail and waved to her.

"Hi, Mom!" As she started to talk, she spotted Mat. "What is Dad doing here? How did he know?"

"I don't know, but let's not let it ruin your day. I love you, Gracie. I'll be right here."

"OK, Mom. I love you too."

As I turned to go back to my seat, I just glared at Mat.

The ceremony was over, and I went into the mass amount of graduates to find Grace.

"Mom! I'm here!" She was with a friend from swimming.

"Come on, honey. I'll take you and your friend for dinner."

"Cool, Mom, thanks." There was no more sign of Mat.

I called my mom the next day.

"Hi, Mom."

"Hi, honey. How did it go?"

"Well, Mat showed up again. How is he finding all of this out?"

"I don't know. Did he talk to you or Grace?"

"No, but just his presence makes things tense. She leaves for college next week, so maybe she won't have to be in all of this…Kathy says the room is almost ready. I'll be coming back to spend some nights with you, Mom."

"Good, honey."

"I'll come this week to your house and spend the night to help."

"OK, I'll see you there."

As the week moved on, I had to move Grace up to college. We had to make two trips because my car wouldn't hold all of it. I finally got her settled in and kissed her good-bye.

We've become like two single girls living alone. I went to my mom's to spend the night and take care of her. She told me that Beth and Karen came all the time and took things out of her house when no one was there. My stomach was sickened at the thought of my mother curled up in a chair, dying, and my sisters are taking her stuff right in front of her. There were tears in her eyes that night and great sadness. "I never thought my children would be like this!" she said.

My heart broke for her that night.

"I want you to go and take some stuff," she told me.

"I will *not*, Mom. I want nothing here except to tell you I love you until I can't anymore. Look around, Mom, is there anything here that you value?"

She was quiet for a few moments and then she said, "No."

"Let them take whatever they want, Mom. Don't let the devil distract you. You have to prepare to go home to God where you belong."

"I can't even pray anymore, Ann."

"Well, that's just the devil, Mom. I'm back now, and I'm going to help you. The devil walked in about nine months ago, but you did not notice. I did though, and I'm here now. Don't let him win!"

The next morning I headed back to work. As I was driving, I realize I was really alone now. Grace and Michael were gone. Not that I have much time to think about it. Grace calls every day, and when I am not between jobs, I was at my mom's.

We were ready to move my mom to Kathy's house now. The room was finished. Beth, Karen, and Jean were not happy at all about the move. When I arrived after work at

Kathy's house to help, it was a mess. Beth and Karen were being horrible. They were bringing mother's clothing over to Kathy's and leaving it on the porch in garbage bags. They would help with nothing. They were like children having a tantrum because they didn't get their way. I stepped over all the mess to find Kathy in the room just about crying.

"Kathy, what is going on?"

"Beth, Karen, and Jean are really giving Mom a hard time. I can't find half her stuff. Things are missing, and they refuse to help."

"Well, Kathy, I don't understand the problem. But let's just get Mom settled in right now."

"I've been working all day at it, Ann."

"OK, I'll help you now. Come on. Let's get the bed together."

Kathy and I worked the rest of the night, but there was still a lot of work to be done. The week went on, and Kathy finally got my mom settled in. It was a real zoo most of the time. People were in and out all the time, phones were ringing, dogs were barking, and my mom stayed up most nights. We were all still spending the nights to help, and caregivers were hired in the daytime. We all had jobs, so it was hard.

Beth was in my mom's room one morning. "Ann, your annulment is final."

"How do you know that, Beth?"

"A letter came from the Archdiocese for you, and I opened it by accident."

"It is more than clearly marked in bold print, Beth. Why did you open my mail?"

"I told you why."

"Well, that's a flat-out lie, Beth. But don't you worry, Beth, God sees everything."

She threw the letter at me and walked away. She was becoming vicious and mean and hateful toward me and Kathy.

Three days later, Kathy called me on my lunch break. "Ann, can you take another night with Mom? Karen is really rough with her and is hurting her."

"WHAT! How does she hurt Mom?"

Kathy told me she was lifting Mom really roughly and putting her down too hard, not being careful.

"Kathy, I don't know how I'll do it, but somehow I will. Mom is in enough pain as it is. She shouldn't be treated like that!" The anger inside me swelled up! My hands were tied, and it was so frustrating. I just wanted to take care of my mom. She was failing fast, and I knew the day was coming quick when she would be gone. I couldn't even bear the thought right now.

It was my night to spend with my mom again. I got there, and my mom was waiting for me. I kissed her and sat down next to her and held her hand. I was tired from work, and it was warm out. "I'm here now, Mom. You can rest. I'll take care of you."

"Thank you, honey, for taking care of me."

"Please, Mom, don't thank me. If I could give you one-hundredth back of what you have given me in my life, I would be doing something, but I can never repay you for being such a wonderful mother."

"Karen told me I was a bad mother."

"Really, when did she tell you this?"

"Yesterday when she was here." Tears were welling up in her eyes and her voice was cracking as she talked.

My anger almost turned to hatred in that moment, but I refused to live that way. Hatred was from the devil, and I wanted nothing to do with it. But, still, I think, *How dare she!* "Maybe, Mom, Karen was a bad daughter. I grew up in the same house, and you were nothing but a loving, giving, selfless mother, especially to Karen who always gave you trouble. Mom, just say the word and I will take a leave of absence from work, and I can take care of you. You can get rid of all these strangers, and you won't have to want for anything."

"Ann, I'll talk to Kathy about it."

"Let me know when you're ready, Mom."

On my way home, I had to stop and see Kyle. We had to start the deposition for the car accident soon. I told him, "OK! But my mother is dying right now, so she will come first, do you understand?"

"Of course, Ann, but I will start the paperwork. These things take time."

My mom was settling into her new digs. Every time I saw her, I could see the time bomb ticking. I know time was growing short. I was so busy with working, Grace, lawsuit, taking care of my mom and my own household chores I could barely think five minutes ahead, but still in the back of my mind, I know the day was coming when she would die, and I love her beyond words!

I was working one night, and my phone rang. I had told my boss that I would only answer the phone if it was my children or about my mom.

"Hello."

"Ann, this is Kathy. Mom is being taken to the hospital. She is throwing up blood."

With great worry in my voice, I said, "I'm on my way." I was right in the middle of serving a huge party, and I knew this would make the staff short, but I didn't even blink an eye. I grabbed my coat and purse. As I was running for the door, I yelled to my boss, "My mom's in the hospital. Got to go!"

I was running to the car, not paying attention to anything. I had one focus, get to my mom! I was finally on the expressway dialing Grace at the same time. "Hi, honey, something is wrong with Grandma. I'll call you when I know more. Love ya." I was driving with speed and caution. Finally I get there. I parked and ran through the emergency room. I found Kathy and I was out of breath.

"What's happening?"

"Mom's lost half the blood in her body. They're transfusing her now. She had a bleed probably in her stomach."

I stood there frozen in my tracks. *Is this the day when my mom dies?* I couldn't bear the thought. Beth, Karen, and Jean were there too. They didn't even talk much to me anymore. Only when they wanted to question me about stuff they wanted to know about.

We waited for hours to see how my mom was. She was finally stable again for the moment. We got her admitted into a room and could talk with her a little bit.

"Are you feeling a little better, Mom?" I asked.

"A little. Who's going to stay with me tonight?"

"Mom, you're in the hospital. There are people here to take care of you."

She was so nervous and scared. She needed someone. "Kathy, I will stay with her," I said.

"Ann, don't you work?"

"Yes, but this is more important. I will call in and cancel work."

"OK, Ann."

"You're OK, Mom. I'll stay with you," I told her. Everyone left and I called Grace to tell her I won't be home. She knew her grandmother needed me and she didn't want her to be left alone either. My mom reached for my hand. "I'm here, Mom."

"Where is Grace, honey?"

"She's at home, Mom."

"Is she alone?"

"Yes, who else is there, Mom?" I knew she didn't like Grace to be alone either, but there was no choice. "You sleep now and let me worry about Grace. I'll be right here."

She closed her eyes and fell asleep. I was so tired, but there's nowhere to even lie down. A few hours went by and I had to go to the bathroom. There's one down the hallway for public use. I looked at my mom, and she was sleeping peacefully, so I went down the hallway, and I was back in five minutes. I walked back to the hospital room, and my mom was awake.

"Ann, where were you?"

"Mom, I've been here all night. I just went to the bathroom. You're OK, Mom."

It was clear to me that my mom should have died that night, but the Lord was not ready for her. After four days in the hospital she came back to Kathy's house. Things seemed to get worse after that. When Jean was in town, she would not spend any nights with my mom—which was where we needed the help—and she would not lift my mom. Karen meanwhile was becoming very mean to my mom. She yelled at her and said very hurtful things to her. She became very rough while handling my mom. And after a while, she just showed up for an hour here and there but no help at all. Beth, though, became the worst. She would not help at all, but she just came and made trouble. Kathy was pulling her hair out. She worked a full-time job as did her husband. I came over on Saturdays after work and gave my mom a shower. Then I stayed the night so Kathy could get some sleep, and I could help my mom some. I no sooner got to work on Sundays then I leave in a couple of hours. I knew my mom and Kathy needed me badly.

One day one of my co-workers started yelling at me because I was leaving shortly after getting there. I was so down and tired, and my heart was so torn up, for I knew time was ticking. I always seemed to be fighting time.

I turned to my co-worker and said, "My sister counts the minutes until I get there. They are at their wits' end, so no job is worth making them wait one more minute." I grabbed my coat and left. When I got to Kathy's house, she was almost in tears. I told her, "Go. I will take the next twenty-four hours." I went to my mom's room.

"I'm here now, Mom. You can rest."

She let out a sigh of relief.

"Come on, I'm going to shower you and get you something to eat. I will change your bed sheets, and you can rest. I will be here all night, OK?"

I knew that she was between worlds and seeing things that no one else saw. Some good and some bad. As evening fell, I told Kathy to take a sleeping pill so she could sleep for the night.

"OK, Ann. I won't get up unless you call for me."

"Kathy, sleep tonight. I'm not going to call you. You need to rest. I'll take care of Mom. Don't worry."

I went back with my mom and sat next to her. "It's me and you, Mom."

"Sounds good, honey."

"Well, let's try to get some sleep."

"Ann, come into bed with me. Please."

"Mom, the bed is not big enough for both of us." I think she just wanted to be held. I pulled up a chair and put my arms around her the best I can. "How is this, Mom?"

"Good!"

It was very uncomfortable, but I knew it comforted her. She often started talking to her sisters who preceded her in death. She asked them to help her. I questioned her about them. What were they doing? Was my dad there? She nodded her head yes or no, but that was it. She knew exactly what I was talking about. She was very clear. Something always stopped her from talking to me.

The next day Kathy got up for work and talked to me. "Ann, we need more help. Jean, Karen, and Beth won't even come anymore, and the daytime workers are not really doing a good job. I think we need to hire someone for the night shift."

"Kathy, that will cost $20 an hour for people. I know. Kathy, I will take a leave of absence from my jobs. Please hire me for $10 an hour, so I can take care of mom. That's all I want to do is take care of her, but I'm alone, and I have to play my bills somehow."

"Ann, I will ask Mom what she wants."

"Fine, Kathy, let me know."

Kathy called me back that night. "Ann, I talked with Mom. I told her we could hire a new person to stay the nights with her or that you would take a leave of absence from your jobs and you would come for half of the money. She didn't care about the money. She just wants her daughter with her. When do you want to start, Ann?"

"I will start tomorrow. Have you told Beth, Karen, and Jean?"

"Yes, they are having a fit but—oh well, they are not helping at all."

"OK. Well, I will pack for a week, and I will be there tomorrow."

I called my jobs, and they were all very supportive. Grace had left for college now. I arrived the next day with suitcase in hand. Kathy had a look of relief on her face when I arrived. We were both exhausted, but this was going to take teamwork. "Kathy, you can go to work now and not worry. I will be here, and I will take care of Mom. We'll work together at night."

"I think this will work better, Ann."

I went to my mother's room. "I'm here, Mom, and I will be here all week. You don't have to worry."

"Thank God!"

That evening we settled in. We tried to feed Mom, but she did not each much. I wanted to shower her, but she just didn't want to. I told Kathy to go to bed and got some sleep. "I'll stay with Mom."

I settled Mom into bed, and I sat right next to her. She just looked around and stared a lot. "Mom, what are you looking at?" She won't answer. I turned on a light. "Would you like to talk for a while?"

"OK, Ann."

"What do you want to talk about, Mom?"

In a soft voice she said, "Ann, would you please sing to me?"

I looked into her big chocolate brown eyes, fighting back my tears and choking up. "Sure, Mom, I'll sing to you." Now at this point it was 2:30 in the morning, and I was tired. I thought to myself, *What song do I know the words to?* I started to sing, "On Eagles' Wings," a beautiful church song. My voice was cracking and tears were running down my face. "I'm sorry, Mom. I wish I had the voice of an angel to sing to you." I knew she was looking for comfort, and I was trying, but my heart was breaking right in half. I wiped away my tears. "Come on, Mom. Let's try to sleep a little. I love you, Mom." I kissed her hand and covered her up. "Now, I'm right here if you need me."

"OK, honey."

The next morning started early. Kathy was getting ready for work already. We now had to lift my mom onto the toilet, so mornings start very physically. Hospice was coming to give her a sponge bath later. The cancer had gone to her bones now, and it hurt her to even move, so a shower just wasn't going to happen anymore. As Kathy was leaving for work, I said, "Don't worry. I'm here now. I'll call you if I need you."

"OK, Ann."

The house never seemed to be quiet. The phone rang about every twenty minutes, the dogs were barking all the time, people were walking in and out every half hour; it was crazy. I tried to feed her some soft oatmeal for breakfast, but all I could get her to eat was about three teaspoons full. "We'll try some more later, Mom."

Hospice came to give her a sponge bath. I was just going to stand by and watch—until they start to hurt my mom. Then I went into protect mode, just like a mother bear with her cub. "You both are moving too slow." Then I started barking out orders. "You, grab that sheet. You, pull this under her. You, move her slowly. Back!" etc. My mom's eyes met mine as if to say, "Help me."

"I've got you, Mom!"

I think the hospice workers were immune to people's pain. I tried to stop the pain in her any way I could. The workers were leaving, and one of them turned to me and said, "You should work for hospice." I shoved them out and tried to get my mom to sleep for a while.

While she slept, I tried to stay close to her room so I could listen for her call. Kathy called about once every hour to check in. I kept reassuring her so she could work as peacefully as possible at the doctor's office where she was the manager. My mom sometimes woke up and wanted to talk a little. I stopped everything when she did because I knew the day was coming when I won't be able to talk to her anymore.

"Do you feel a little better now that you've slept some?"

"Yes, honey."

"Good."

I had to call Kathy once in a while to come home to help lift her on the toilet. I was so afraid of dropping her. In between everything, there was all the rest of the chores. Laundry, meals, clean up, etc. The day flew by, and by night, I was totally spent. I had a day bed to sleep close to my mom.

I knew something was terrorizing her because she never wanted to be alone, even for a minute; but whatever it was, it was between worlds and would not allow her to talk. I was watching for signs from her.

The next day I was cleaning the room while she sat up for a while. I pushed the flat-screen TV backward and out of the way. She sighed a sigh of relief. I looked at her and noticed it seemed as if something had been interrupted. I went and sat down by her. "Mom, when they come again, call me, OK?"

She nodded yes.

An hour later, she called out to me, "Ann, they're back." She was very clear in her words and thoughts.

"OK, Mom. I'm right here." I went over and kissed her on the cheek, sat down next to her, and put my arms around her. "I love you, Mom." She held my hand. I took some holy water and blessed her. I finally understood so much of what was making her afraid. Even though I couldn't do much I could at least hold her and be there. She took great comfort in this.

Kathy came home that night, and I told her all of this. I was due to leave the next morning for a day. I had to finish one more day of work and get some clean clothes. Workers were to come and stay with my mom until I come back.

Kathy and I got up, and my mom was really bad. She did not want us to leave her. Kathy said, "Ann, I will try to call Beth to see if she will help."

"OK, Kathy."

She called Beth and asked her to come, but Beth would have no part of it.

"Kathy, we can't leave her like this. Call and cancel the workers. I will call in off work. I don't care if they fire me. You go to work, and we'll figure this out tonight."

I looked at my mom and said, "I'm going to stay with you, Mom. Don't worry." She seemed to relax a little. The day just became crazier. Kathy left for work, and I tried to feed my mom something. She didn't want food. She started calling out her oldest sister's name over and over and over. Her sister's name was Gema, and she was calling her Gem. I sat next to her and finally I said, "Do you want me to call Aunt Gem, Mom?"

She nodded yes. I dialed the phone. "Aunt Gem, this is Ann. Please can you say something to my mom. She keeps calling for you."

"Sure."

I put the phone to hear ear and I could hear Gem say, "You're suffering. Please try to rest." I took the phone back and thanked her. Aunt Gem was caring for her husband who was very ill and dying as well.

My mom started again calling out for Aunt Gem, almost to the point of driving me crazy. "OK, Mom, I'll call her again…Aunt Gem, please talk to her again. She keeps calling for you. I think she's trying to tell you something." Again, I heard her telling my mom, "Oh, God bless you, you are suffering."

I thanked her and hung up again. My mom started saying, "Gem, water. Gem, water." I kept trying to give her a drink of water, and she pushed it away and called out again, "Gem, water!" over and over again.

"Mom, I don't know what you want."

"Water, Gem!"

At that moment, I looked to her nightstand and saw a small bottle of holy water. I picked it up and showed it to her. "Do you mean holy water?"

She looked at it and said, "Gem, holy water." She then started calling out for her other sister, Josephine. Over and over again, but this time I was more aware. I called Aunt Jo and she talked to my mom for a minute but was crying too hard to continue. Kathy called at this time and told me hospice was coming to give my mom a bath again.

"No way, Kathy, not today. I will call and cancel it. Mom is not going through that today."

"OK, Ann. That's fine."

The day was flying by. Karen called. "How's Mom, Ann?"

"She's terrible. You need to come see her today, Karen."

"No, maybe on the weekend. I've got to go."

It was about three in the afternoon, and things became very quiet for the first time in a long time. I started to sing the chaplets of divine mercy, which were prayers, over my mother while holding her hand. I sang them with no interruption at all, which had never happened. When I was done, I went over to the picture of Jesus on the wall, bowed, and then I began to talk. "Dear Lord, I believe in you and trust in you. I believe in these prayers and the promises they hold. I love you, Lord!" I went back to my mom. "Mom, take my hand. Remember, wherever you go, I love you!"

"I love you too, Ann. He's coming soon."

I knew in my heart it was coming. That final hour, but not yet. "I'm going to clean up a little before Kathy gets home, OK?"

I started to clean the room from the day's mess. My mom called out to me, "Ann, don't touch the horn!"

"Don't touch the horn?"

"Yes, don't touch the horn!"

I stopped what I was doing and sat down next to her. She pointed to the corner of the room. "Mom, who put the horn there? Did Jesus put it there?"

She nodded her head yes.

"Mom, this is the horn that will blow when you wake up on the other side of death. You will rise to this! Come on, you've had a long day, and I'm going to get you into bed for a while."

She seemed to sleep but very restlessly. Kathy came home, and she and I talked. "Kathy, we can't leave her anymore with anyone but us."

"I know, Ann."

"Kathy, I'm going to leave tonight. I'll go pack a suitcase, take a shower, see Grace, and I will be back tomorrow by twelve noon. Can you hold down the fort until then?"

"Yes, Ann."

Just then Beth walked in. She sat down next to my mom on the bed. My mom opened her eyes and said, "Get out!" My mother never had spoken like that. I was not sure what she was seeing at this point, but whatever it was, it wasn't good. It was starting to get dark out, and I had a long car ride ahead of me. Kathy kept telling me to go. Beth was really being mean to us, as well; she wasn't answering when we talked to her.

"OK, Kathy, I'll be back tomorrow by noon," I told her. I kissed my mom good-bye and whispered in her ear,

"I'll be back tomorrow." I turned to Kathy: "Don't leave her tonight." I drove home thinking of the day. I was worn out. I got home and just passed out.

In the morning about 8:00 a.m., Kathy called. "Ann, Mom passed away this morning."

I didn't even cry at that point. I just became very quiet. I had known it was close, but I thought a couple more weeks.

"Were you with her, Kathy?"

"No, we went to bed, and she was resting. She called out for you, Ann, and then she was quiet. I thought she went back to sleep. All night I thought she was finally sleeping well, and I was excited to tell you when you came. When I got up, she was gone."

"I will pack some clothes for the next few days and a dress for the funeral, and I'll be over."

I called Grace at school to let her know. She had to make arrangements to be home. Michael was home already between college and a summer job.

I was now trying to pack quickly. Kathy's twenty-year-old daughter Brittany called me. "Aunt Ann." She was sobbing. "Please hurry, Aunt Beth and Aunt Karen are ripping my mother apart."

"I'm coming as fast as I can."

By the time I got to Kathy's house, they had already taken my mother's body away and everyone had left. It was just Kathy and me. "How bad was it this morning?" I asked her.

"Karen and Beth were wicked. I was sobbing, and they just were horrid. The next few days are going to be tough to get through."

"We'll do the best we can. Kathy, I have done Mom's makeup and hair for the last thirty years. I want to do it for the last time. I don't want her to look bad in her coffin."

"That's fine, Ann. I will make arrangements with the funeral home then."

We all had to go to the funeral home to finalize the arrangements. I had gone a month earlier by myself and set up most of it already, but there were still some small details to be taken care of. Later that morning, Beth, Karen, Kathy, and I met with the funeral director. Jean was on her way into town. I had told the funeral director the first time I met him that I thought there might be problems come funeral time. He said he was used to it, so I didn't worry. We sat down at a long table, Karen and Beth on one side and Kathy and I on the other side. Within ten minutes, Beth was yelling at everyone, Karen was putting her two cents in, and the funeral director was turning pale with shock.

I knew tension was high and nerves were raw. I knew things were about to get ugly. I turned to the funeral director and asked if we could have a few minutes alone. He pretty much ran out of the room. Beth erupted into a full-blown rage, mostly at Kathy and me. I was just numb. I really didn't care anymore. I almost didn't hear them. I just wanted it over! Finally, we took care of the funeral and leave.

I stayed with Kathy that night. We had known things were getting bad, but we never thought it would be this bad.

The next morning I was to go do my mother's hair and makeup in her coffin. I knew it would be hard, but it would have meant a lot to her. I was preparing to go when Grace called me. "Mom, Dad called me, and he's coming both days of the funeral. How did he find out about Grandma's death? Who told him, Mom?"

"Grace, calm down, honey. I don't know how he found out. Just call him and tell him what you want."

"NO, Mom. I don't want to talk to him."

"I know, honey. He's not coming to the funeral for Grandma, she's dead. He's not coming to support me. We're divorced. He's coming to see you and Michael. Don't you see, this is how he can force you to talk to him."

"Mom, you call him."

"Grace, I really don't want him here either. My mother is dead, and I just want to grieve quietly. I don't want him in my face. OK, I will call him, and I'll take care of it. I'll see you and Michael tomorrow."

"OK, Mom. I love you."

Kathy had been listening the whole time. "Ann, are you going to call Mat?"

"Yes, I am. He is no longer a part of this family. Who told him?!"

"I don't know."

I tried to calm myself before calling. All right, I just had to do it. I picked up the phone and called. "Hello? Mat, this is Ann. Grace said you called and left a message that you will be at the funeral."

"Yes, I did."

"How did you know my mother was dead?"

"Your sisters—Beth, Karen, and Jean—told me. They have been telling me everything right along."

Another sword went through my heart. How could my sisters betray me and my children so much? Weren't we hurt enough? They had kicked us in our guts while we were down on our knees. "Well, Mat, I guess now I have to deal with you and my sisters, but first you. I am asking you—no, I'm begging you, to leave us grieve my mother's death in peace and stay away. But if you don't, I will play my trump card in this game and have you removed from the funeral home. You will turn my mother's funeral into a circus. Please don't come."

"Ann, I will do whatever I please!"

"Bring it, Mat! I'm ready for you!" I slammed the phone down. Kathy came and hugged me. "I need to go and do Mom's hair. I'll be back." I was so hurt and mad at my sisters.

I arrived at the funeral home in the early afternoon. The funeral director knew me from the day before. "Hi, Ann, how are you doing?"

"I'm OK. Just trying to get through the next few days."

"Well, I see what you're up against."

"I'm sure it's going to get worse."

"Do you want me to go into the room with you, Ann?"

"No, thank you. I would like to be alone with my mom."

"OK, then, just through those doors."

I took a deep breath and walked in. I could see her lying in the coffin in the dress I had bought for her. I walked up to her and started crying quietly to myself. After about five minutes, I dried my tears and said, "Well, Mom, this is the last time I do your hair and makeup, and I'm off-duty." When I was finished, she looked more beautiful in death than in life. This was true, I knew, she went home to God. I talked for a little bit to her and then I said, "I love you, Mom. Please pray for me. I'll see you soon," and I left. Emotionally, I was drained; and physically, I didn't have much more.

The next day the funeral began. The first hour was for family only. I had my time alone the day before. I was very nervous that Mat would show up, and so were Grace and Michael. Beth, Karen, and Jean were all in foul moods and were being nasty to everyone. People started coming in, and time seemed to move quickly. Dana, Mary, and Wendy all came to be with me. They knew how crazy my sisters were behaving toward me, so they had come to support me and my children. I didn't have time to cry or even grieve. I just had to forge forward. I kept waiting for Mat to come and make me crazy. He had told Beth, Jean, and Karen that I had barred him from coming to the funeral; and all they wanted to do was hurt me and my kids. The funeral director already had been alerted and was ready for what might come. The day flew by, and before I knew it, it was over and there was no sign of Mat.

The mass started early the next day. It was sad to look around at everyone who had gathered one more time for my mom, and I knew things would never be the same after today. Just as the mass was about to end, they wheeled her coffin by me one last time. My spirit was so low. I gently reached out and touched it as it went by, trying to choke back my tears with no success at all. We lay her to rest next to my dad and finished with a luncheon that day. Michael took Grace back to school and headed home. I had to stop back at Kathy's to pick up my things. Kathy and I were both quiet. I gave her a hug and said, "I'll call tomorrow. I have one more day off work."

"OK, Ann, be careful going home."

It was an hour's drive, and I was looking forward to being alone and just quiet.

The next day Beth and Jean went to Kathy's house and started trouble. Kathy called later to tell me about the yelling and screaming that went on. "Beth and Jean are out of control, and Karen was right behind them."

"Kathy, you know they want our blood for some reason, and they won't stop until they get it!"

"I think you're right, Ann."

"Kathy, Mom's gone, and I really don't ever want to see Beth, Jean, and Karen again. I'm done! If people are here to tear me and my kids down, they need to go."

The next day I returned to work. Back to my crazy schedule. I fell back in the grind just like a robot. A couple weeks went by and Dana called me. "Hey, Ann, guess who called me today?"

"Um, I don't know."

"Mat called."

"What did he want?"

"Well, I told him before he spoke that I was your friend. He said then that he should just hang up."

"Dana, I bet he was going to ask you to spy on us."

"Probably."

"He can't get to me through my sisters anymore, so now he's coming after my friends. I wish he would just go away already. Well, now, I have to keep my eyes open and be ready for what's next."

Three weeks later Grace called me. "Hi, Mom."

"Hi, Grace."

"Guess who wants to friend me on Facebook."

"Who, Grace?"

"Dad's friend Robert."

"OK, that's just weird, honey. It's your dad trying to spy on us."

"I know, Mom. It's creepy!"

"Just block him, honey, and stay away. When you're ready to make peace with your dad, you will."

Another two weeks passed almost to the day. Grace called me just out of control.

"Honey, what's wrong?"

"Mom, what is he trying to do?"

"Slow down, Grace."

"Mom, let me read this to you."

"'Hello, Grace, my name is Sandy Latrell, and I am your dad's new girlfriend. I would like to meet you and know you better.' What is he doing, Mom?"

"Grace, I would answer back like this: 'Gee, Sandy, you must have the wrong person because my dad is GAY!'"

"Mom, I don't want to answer at all."

"Well, then don't. Just block her. He'll soon get the picture."

I hung up and called Michael.

"Hi, Mom."

"Hi, honey. Did you get an email from a Sandy—"

"Oh, from Dad's new girlfriend, yeah, weird, ha."

"What are you going to do, Michael?"

"Block it, Mom. I don't want to open that can of worms."

"Are you sure?"

"Yes, Mom, I'm sure."

"OK."

When I hung up the phone, I knew Michael, Grace, and I needed time to heal from the wounds of all of this. With my mom not even cold in her grave and the weight of everything else that had gone on, the wounds were bigger than ever, but still the bills had to be paid and there was no time to rest. I tried to talk with Grace and Michael as much as possible to try to get them to vent. Sometimes it helped and sometimes it just seemed to make things worse. Work seemed to bury me; it was really taking its toll on me now. How much longer could I keep this pace up?

CHAPTER 12

The Lawsuit

MY LAWYER, KYLE, CALLED ME. "Ann, the lawsuit for the car accident is about to settle. Where have you been?"

"My mom passed away, Kyle."

"Ann, I'm so sorry. Why didn't you call me?"

"I'm sorry, Kyle. I just had a few too many things on my plate to deal with, and my mind wasn't thinking."

"I would have come, Ann."

"I know, Kyle."

"We need to get together, Ann, by next week to start to finalize this."

"I'm ready, Kyle. I'll be there."

I was excited to end this lawsuit. It had dragged on for a long time. It had been like a rock tied around my neck. The car accident had left me with a lot of damage to my body for the rest of my life. It was what it was, and I had learned to work with it, but it had left me a weaker person. I stopped in at church. It was the middle of the day. I sat in a pew near the altar. It's quiet and peaceful here. I started to talk to the lord. "Thank you, my lord, for bringing me through this very hard time. Please, Lord, take my hand and don't let it go until you see me safe in heaven with you. You are my one true love, Lord, but I am so lonely here on earth. Please, Lord, look over the earth and find a good man for me. You take my problems, Lord, and you deal with them. I love you, Lord!" I sat for a while in the quiet by myself, and then I left.

Three days later, Kyle called. "Ann, the lawsuit is settled. You won."

"Kyle, all I did was tell the truth as to what happened."

"Well, can you come in tomorrow and pick up your check from the insurance companies?"

"I will be there." I hung up the phone and fell to my knees. "Thank you, my Father in heaven, for all that you do for me."

The next day Kyle and I met. "Well, Ann, it is done. Here is your check. What do you think you'll do with the money?"

"Kyle, I have been able to pay my bills by the skin of my teeth. I have kept a roof over my family's head and food on the table by the grace of God. This money will pay off the house and the used Ford Taurus I bought when Grace took her car to college. I always promised Michael could have LASIK eye surgery, and now I can afford it. Also, I can pay for my new front door and get rid of the bill. After that, there's not much left. A small amount to save for the next bend in the river of my life. It will lower my bills some, but at least they won't be able to take the house or the car."

"Wow, Ann, I've seen a lot of people walk out of here with big checks and go blow it all on vacations, clothes, boats, cars, and then they are broke in a year."

"Well, Kyle, I'm not a lot of people! I need to think about a future wherever God may lead me."

"You're a strong woman, Ann."

"I am nothing without God's hand in mine, but with him, I can do anything!"

I gave Kyle a hug and thanked him for everything. It was like closing a part of my life.

The first thing I did the next day was go to the bank to arrange to pay the mortgage and car note off. It took a week to process all the paperwork and the transfers of money, but when it was time for the final signature on the paperwork, Grace and I went together. When we came out of the bank, Grace put her arm around me and said, "I'm proud of you, Mom! Go ahead and do a dance of joy."

I laughed out loud and did a dance in front of the bank. The bank manager looked out the window and smiled. It's good when we get a moment in life, but it's great when we can share it with others. It lifted some weight off my shoulders, that's for sure.

Mary called me daily now. We had become great friends, even better than before. I am so thankful to have her in my life again. I seemed as if I was at work all the time. I was so lonely especially since my mom was gone and my family all torn up. Grace was at school most of the time, and Michael was in and out. I came home from work one night and sat in the dark looking out the window. I just wanted to cry, but I thought to myself, *No more tears.* I needed to start living again.

As time went on, I started to prepare myself to date again. *Gosh, I don't even think I know how to kiss anymore.* I was terrified! Dating had changed since my youth, not to mention how many creepy guys were out there, and I was a little naïve. I was not too much different than most women, thinking if I dated I would be dragged into a house and raped or killed. I thought, *OK, I can sit on the curb and be afraid or I can push forward and live. Well, I choose life!* So forward I went. It wasn't long before I was going out on my first date. A man I met on a dating site. We talked for a while and then decided to meet. I told Mary and Dana where we would be so someone will know. Kathy made me promise to call right when I got back. Everyone was nervous for me and me too! We met finally in a restaurant and it was so uncomfortable for both of us. There was no connection at all. I was bored and really turned off. The anger welled up inside of me, and I became mad at Mat when I thought of how he put me in this spot. When the date ended, I went to the restroom and called Mary from a stall. "This is humiliating, Mary."

"Oh, Ann, I'm sorry. It will get better."

"I'm going home tonight and lock the doors and eat some ice cream."

I soon got back up on my horse and started dating again. I was meeting some very unique men. I quickly understood the saying, "You have to kiss a lot of toads before you find your prince." The way this was going, I was sure my prince died a long time ago, but I pushed forward. I would go to dinner with a man or talk to him for a while, but there was no real connection. It was such a game, and I hated it.

I was starting to have pains in my stomach enough that it was time to see a doctor. I had no health insurance but I saved up money and went anyway. Doctor after doctor after doctor. No one could find the problem. The medical bills mounted quickly. Still I was working and dating through it all. The fifth doctor I saw sent me to a specialist. It took me three months to get an appointment, and I was sure the bill was going to be high. Finally, the sixth doctor saw me. After he examined me and did some testing, he sat to talk with me. "Ann, there is something wrong but I just don't know what. I'm going to send you to a friend of mine."

"Are you kidding me! That will be my seventh doctor with no answer. It took me three months to see you. I will be dead by the time he sees me."

"If I can get you in in two days, will you go see him?"

"OK, two days!"

Now I was wearing down about this point, but I went to see the seventh doctor. He came in and asked a few questions and then examined me. "OK," he said, "come in my office and we'll talk."

Wow, that was quick, I thought. I went to his office.

"Have a seat, Ann," he said. "Ann, you have a tear in your abdominal wall."

"WHAT!"

"Don't be alarmed. People walk around with them all the time and don't even know they have them."

"Well, how do you fix it?"

"Surgery."

All I could think of was I have no health insurance, and I was alone. How could I be off work that long, but this needed to be fixed.

"Well, let's schedule it and work out the details."

"OK, Ann. I can do surgery in eight weeks."

"OK, it's a date."

CHAPTER 13

Meeting Tom Hawkins

EVEN THOUGH THERE WERE PEOPLE around me to help, I left there feeling so alone. Now I was dating three different men at the same time, and tried to connect but just dating. Michael said he would go with me to surgery and stay with me, which made me feel better.

Now I had to prepare. Between working and dating, there wasn't much time, but I had to clean my bedroom and bleach everything for when I come home from surgery. Bills had to be paid and surgery was right after the New Year, so the holidays were wrapped up in there too. I clipped along to get things done in time. I had three weeks before surgery, and I was on my way to work. I had a rebate check in my purse from a major food chain store. It's been there for three weeks now, and I needed to take care of it. I was fighting with myself to stop and deal with it or just keep going to work. Well, deal with it wins. I pulled into the parking lot, parked, and ran in. I only had about twenty minutes. I quickly got in the line for customer service. There were several employees helping take care of customers so things were moving, but were they moving fast enough? I heard someone calling, "Ma'am, can I help you?"

I walked to the man behind the counter. "I would like to cash this check, please."

"Before you cash the check, there is a special deal going on right now you might be interested in."

He started right into his sales pitch, but all I could think about was I was going to be late for work. "OK, OK, sign me up."

He started typing my information into the computer. "You really should put your children or your spouse on this with you," he said.

I looked at him and said, "I don't have a spouse, but how clever of you to find that out."

He flashed me a big toothy smile and said, "Well, I am a widower."

We both laughed a little, and I replied, "Oh, the widower card, that's a good one."

He seemed to be typing slower now, and I needed to go. I knew he's flirting with me, and it's fun, but I was becoming late. He started again. "Do you play cards?"

"What? Cards?"

"Well, ever since my wife passed away, I'm always third man out and the card club that I was in doesn't invite me anymore.'

"I do hate third man out!"

"Would you just come and play cards as my partner?"

"Sure, it sounds like fun."

"My name is Tom."

"Hi, Tom. I'm Ann. Tom, I really have to go."

"OK, Ann. Here, give me your phone number and here is mine."

"Great. Here you go. Nice to meet you. I've got to go." I walked away knowing he was watching me walk away. I threw his phone number in my purse and ran to work.

The next day at work I was cleaning out my purse. It was a slow morning, so I was multitasking. I was not looking forward to going home to an empty nest tonight. I was in a restless mood. I picked up the phone and called him. He did not answer, so I left this message: "Hi, Tom, this is Ann. I met you yesterday. I was wondering if you would like to get a cup of coffee tonight and talk. Let me know."

I put the phone number back in my purse and forgot about it. Little did I know, Tom had already tried to call me seven times that morning with no success. By midafternoon, I left work and went home. I was tired so I lay down for a while. The phone rang. "Hi, Ann. This is Tom."

"Hello, Tom."

"Ann, would you like to have dinner with me tonight?"

"Sure, that sounds great. I'll meet you at the restaurant on the corner of Main Street and Vine at 8:00 p.m."

"See you there."

I hung up the phone and thought, *How did he get my home phone number?*

I got up and called Mary because I always wanted someone to know where I was when I was on a date. I soon got ready and left. When I got to the restaurant, Tom was not there yet, but the men's golf league from the country club where I work was there having a private party. About twenty of them! Just then Tom walked in.

"Hi, Ann."

"Hi, Tom."

At this moment several of the golfers noticed that I was there. "Ann! What are you doing here?"

"Well, I—"

"Hey, Ann's here. Come on in."

"No thank you. You guys have fun. My friend and I are going to eat."

As we were walking to our table, another golfer was there eating. "Ann, hi!"

"Oh, how are you tonight?"

I thought to myself, *Tom must think I know every man here, and I'm a party girl.* We finally sat down. He ordered dinner for us with some wine. I was glad because I needed a glass by this time to relax.

I asked him, "Tom, how did you get my home phone number?"

"Ann, I called the number you gave me seven times and nothing. See, look." He held up his cell phone and showed me the calls. "So I gave it one more chance and went to the White Pages and looked you up, and you were there."

"Let me see that number I gave you, Tom."

He showed me the number. I started to laugh.

"What's so funny?"

"Tom, I gave you my son's cell phone number by accident. I am so sorry, but I'm glad you were persistent."

He told me all about his wife's death and how sad it was, but now it was time to move on. "So, Ann, I've told you my story. How about you?"

"We don't need to talk about that, Tom."

"No, no. Come on, Ann."

"OK, Tom, but we're going to need a lot more wine then." I laughed. As I was telling him my story, his mouth dropped open and his eyes were open wide. Kind of a stunned look. I thought to myself, "And we're done!" We closed out the restaurant that night. Tom walked me to my car, gave me a little hug, and asked if he could see me again. Sure!

We met again four days later for dinner. I was preparing for surgery, and I knew I had to tell Tom, but I hardly knew him. We ordered a drink with dinner and that seemed to make us both relax. As we were talking, I brought up my surgery. "Tom, I will be down for a while so don't think I'm blowing you off."

"Can I come see you in the hospital, Ann?"

"No, but when I get home, you can come."

It felt nice to have someone care about me. We laughed all the way through dinner. Tom walked me to my car. "Ann, can I kiss you?"

"Yes, Tom, you can."

At that moment, it was snowing big chunky white snowflakes. Tom put his hands on the sides of my face and kissed me so tenderly with snowflakes gently hitting our faces. I felt like we were in a movie. That first kiss would tell you a lot about your feelings.

The next morning Tom e-mailed me. "Dear Ann, I had a very nice time last night. I'm sorry for kissing you so long, but I couldn't let go. Could we have dinner one more time before you go into surgery? Tom."

I smiled. I e-mailed back: "Dear Tom, I had a very nice time too. You were every bit a gentleman and that is rare to find today. Your kiss was lovely and sweet. I enjoyed it very much. Call me and we'll make dinner plans. Ann."

Tom called me later that night, and we talked for an hour. He asked me to dinner at his house before I went into surgery. *Gosh, a man who can cook! Be still my heart.* We set the day for the third day of the New Year.

Now Grace had been watching all of this. "Mom, are you going to his house?"

"Yes, for dinner."

"Mom, you don't even know this man that well. Let's at least drive by the front of his house first."

"OK. Let's go now."

Grace and I drove over to Tom's house like two schoolgirls checking up on their boyfriends. We drove by a very nice house. "Well, Grace, I don't think he's an ax murderer."

"Mom, he's either a creeper or a keeper!"

"Got it."

I did feel a little better when we drove by though. I let Mary and Kathy know where I was going to be as well.

The night was here. I walked up to the front door and knocked. Tom opened the door. "Hi, Ann, come on in."

"Wow, dinner smells good."

The house was clean and well-kept. He had made a very nice dinner with some lovely wine, which of course relaxed us so much we made out like teenagers. When I first met Tom, I wasn't that attracted to him. He was about six-foot, slender, bald on top with salt-and-pepper hair around the sides, small oval glasses with brown eyes and a squared-off chin. Now I found myself taking a few more looks.

Tom called every night up to the day of surgery. Michael took me to surgery that day. He was wonderful. The surgery was supposed to clear up some scar tissue from an old hysterectomy. It was supposed to take an hour.

When I came to and was able to talk, the doctor told me the surgery took four hours. Someone along the way put my colon in backward and upside down and scar tissue grew over it and froze it to my abdominal wall. When they were pulling the scar tissue off, they made a hole in my bladder and had to stitch it up. I had to wear a catheter for a week. The doctor asked me how I had lived like that for the past ten years.

Now I had to leave the hospital that day due to no health insurance. Michael tried to feed me Jell-O and ice chips, but we had a long ride home. He packed me in the car very carefully and took care to drive slowly. When we reached home, my bedroom was ready. It was cleaned and ready for me to crawl into bed. I was so weak. Grace came home from school that night to help. Within six hours of her being home, she started to throw up. She had the flu.

"Grace, you have to go back to school, honey. I can't catch this right now."

"I know, Mom. I'm sorry."

"Michael will follow you, and we'll make you some homemade chicken soup, and he'll bring it back tonight. You go and get some sleep now."

"OK, Mom. I'll call later."

Tom called every night and talked to me until I fell asleep. One night he asked, "Ann, would it be all right if I bring lunch over for you?"

"Not yet, Tom. I'm not ready to see you." I still had the catheter in, and I didn't want anyone over.

Tom called one night, and we were talking. I was due to get the catheter out the next day. We hung up about 10:00 p.m. I went to the bathroom and noticed some blood. I was bleeding from the surgery. Hemorrhaging. I waited for an hour, thinking it was something small. Finally, I called for Michael and told him.

"Mom, call the doctor!"

Right. I finally got a hold of him and told him what's going on. "Ann, you probably just tore some stitches. I could meet you at the hospital, or you could just come to the office tomorrow morning."

By this time, it was 2:00 a.m. already. "I'll wait till morning."

"OK, I'll see you then."

I continued to bleed all night. Dana was supposed to take me later in the day, but I called her at 7:30 a.m. and told her to come now. The bathroom looked like homicide happened there. There was blood everywhere. I called for Michael. He came in the bathroom and looked around. "MOM! It's time to go to the hospital."

"Dana is on her way, Michael. I'm doing OK." I could see the worry on his face.

Just then Dana arrived. "I'm ready, Ann."

I thought about all the ivory leather interior of her car and said, "Dana, I think we will need a blanket."

She looked at the bathroom. "Oh my god, Ann. Let's go."

Michael brought a blanket and tucked me in. We got to the doctor's, and I was weak from the blood loss. The doctor came in. "How are you, Ann?"

"Well. I think the bleeding has stopped, but this catheter needs to come out."

"I will take it out right now."

What a relief. Now what?

"You must have torn a stitch or two, but it looks as if it sealed itself off. Go home and rest now. If you have any more trouble, call me."

I was so weak that my body was shaking. Dana scooped me up and drove me home.

Tom texted me asking how the doctor's visit went. I texted back how I had hemorrhaged and was weak. He had no idea as to what went on after we hung up that night. "Oh my god, sweetie, are you OK? I will call you tonight, Ann."

Michael got dinner for me and took care of me the rest of the night. The phone rang around 8:00 p.m. Michael answered it. He brought me the phone. "It's your boyfriend." That's weird, to hear someone say "boyfriend."

"Hello, Tom."

"Ann, how are you feeling?"

"Weak and shaky."

"Can I come tomorrow and bring lunch?"

"Well, Tom, I'm not going to be doing much of anything."

"That's OK, Ann."

"OK. No one is going to be here with me anyway."

"Great, I'll see you around noon."

When we hung up, I think he's the only one to call or come over. The other guys I was dating never even called. I was done with the rest of them that day. The next day Tom came over. I opened the door to find him standing with lunch and flowers for me. He came in, sat me in a chair, and served us lunch. A healthy lunch of soup and a lean sandwich. No fast food at all. After lunch, we went to sit on the couch. I was still shaking some. Tom grabbed a blanket and wrapped it around me, then he opened his arms and said, "Just get comfortable, Ann. We're just going to talk."

We talked all day into the night just about anything and everything. Once in a while I did fall asleep on his shoulder just for a few minutes, but he doesn't wake me. Finally, Tom said, "OK, I have to go."

"OK, Tom. Before you go, tell me something nice so I can dream about you tonight."

"Ann, I think I am falling in love with you."

"Wow, Tom, that will do it."

He kissed me and left. I did believe that was the night I fell in love with Tom Hawkins.

I continued to get stronger, and before you know it, I was back to work. Tom and I were dating only each other now to see where it would go. He asked me to spend the night at his house with him just to sleep together, nothing else. I was not strong enough yet anyway. We were both lonely just for some touch. I would not bring him to my house because Grace was there, and I did not want to make her uncomfortable or even set that kind of example for her. I was so nervous. Mat was the only man I had been with ever. Tom had a nice dinner ready and some wine with it. We talked, and got into bed. He put his arms around me, and it felt so right to both of us. Mat had never held me like that. We fell asleep in each other's arms. I didn't think either of us had slept that well in a long time. We had several sleepovers after that. Just sleep! It felt wonderful. Tom asked me to move in with him. I laughed and said, "You like it, put a ring on it! I'm a marrying kind of gal."

Tom replied, "I'm not sure if I want to marry."

"That's OK, Tom, if you don't want to marry again, but I do. I don't know if you're the one for me, but I will know within six months' time. And at that time, if you don't want to marry, I will move on. I'm looking to be with someone in marriage, Tom."

"That's fair enough, Ann."

"If you are sure that you don't want to marry, Tom, please cut me loose now and don't break my heart."

"I really don't know what I want, Ann."

"Well, at least you know where I stand."

A few weeks passed. Tom called every night if we weren't together already. We decided to go away for the weekend and consummated our relationship. Tom was a romantic guy and had set up the whole weekend for us. A beautiful hotel room, fabulous dinner at a high-end restaurant, a horse-drawn carriage ride at night, and after-dinner drinks in a high-rise building overlooking the town at night all lit up. What girl couldn't get used to that? We went back to the room and consummated our love. I had never made love to a man who wanted me, only Mat who never wanted me. I felt so alive in Tom's arms. I was falling deeply in love with this man, and he was falling hard too.

It was now Easter and high time Michael and Grace met Tom. We all went to church together and had a nice dinner. They weren't sure what to think, but they knew I had a smile on my face again.

A couple of weeks later, Tom made an appointment to get his hair cut at the salon by me. I called him. "Tom, what are you doing? You don't have to come here for a haircut."

"Ann, I just want to see where you work and meet some of your co-workers."

"OK, Tom, sure."

I knew something was up. He came in, and I introduced him around. Then I cut his hair. It was very busy that night. When I was done, he pretended to be looking for a tip for me and pulled out a beautiful diamond and ruby ring. "Will you marry me, Ann?"

"YES! Tom, I will."

The salon was abuzz. All these women and a man proposing in front of them! It turned into a big party, everyone laughing and hugging. Congratulations all around.

Grace was at school when I called her. "Mom, text me a picture of your ring," she said. "Congratulations, Mom."

"Thanks, honey. Grace, will you be my maid of honor?"

"Really, Mom. I thought you would ask your friend Mary."

"Mary is my really good friend, but you're my daughter and my best girl."

"Thanks, Mom. We have a lot of planning to do."

I went home and told Michael. "Mom, if you're happy, I'm happy."

Then I called Mary to tell her. "Ann, are you sure you want to marry again after all you have gone through with Mat?"

"Mary, I want to get up and live. I'm not going to be so afraid that I just sit here and do nothing. I'm in love with Tom, and he loves me. The next step for me is marriage."

CHAPTER 14

My New Life

I QUIT MY COUNTRY CLUB job so I could have time to work, plan a wedding, combine houses, and take care of my own home. Time flew. It was so nice to be in love. Finally, it was here. On a beautiful fall day, Tom and I were married in a small church full of family and friends watching. The only thing missing was my mom. Never did I think I could be this happy again in my life. But there was God sending me just exactly what I asked Him for. A good man who will love me as much as I love him.

When we came back from our honeymoon, Michael was ready to move out on his own. He had grown into a young man I was proud of. It's time for him to spread his wings and fly! I had done the best I could to prepare him for life. It's still hard to let him go, but I knew this day would come, and I looked forward to watching him grow in his adult life and what he would become. Grace would be graduating from college in the spring. She was growing into a very nice young woman. It's going to be a big adjustment for her to be here with me and Tom. Changes were all around. It's the new normal we all had to adjust to. Still it's important that Grace saw her mom happy. She had gone through most of the worst with me. I looked forward to her becoming the woman I think she will become. A smart, kind, compassionate, strong woman.

As for Mat, he still lived a life of denial that he's gay. He had moved out of state to be back with his family. That's what he always wanted to do. He dated unsuspecting women just to look heterosexual. He had gone back to the cage, which he locked himself in, and I was afraid he had locked the door forever. There would always be a part of my heart that loves Mat, and a part of my heart would always be sorrowful that he's not at peace with who he was. I would bear the huge scar that he had left on my heart forever. I think only God can fix that someday.

Tom and I will start a new chapter in our lives. He fills the hole in my heart with the love he gives me. He is a man who loves me for the woman I am. I look forward to growing old with him, laughing a lot and loving all the way.

Someday when it is my turn to leave this earth, I pray that my father in heaven will bring me home and unite me with all who have gone before me. When I see my mom again in heaven, I'm sure she will say to me, "What took you so long, honey?"

I look back and I can see clearly now the bends in the river of my life and most importantly that through everything God always had me in the palm of his hand. I don't know what lies ahead, but I look forward to my journey! The end, or until the river bends again.

ABOUT THE AUTHOR

Ann DeChellis was born and raised in Michigan. She is the daughter of first generation Italian parents who raised her with old world values and a strong will, Ann is one of a kind.

CPSIA information can be obtained at www.ICGtesting.com
Printed in the USA
BVOW04s2152140615

404619BV00001B/9/P